GALLOWAY

TRAINING
PROGRAMS

Library of Congress Cataloging in Publication Data

Galloway, Jeff, 1945-**Galloway Training**

1. Running. 2. Running-Training. 3. Fitness-Health. I. Title

ISBN: 0-9647187-4-X

First Printing: 2007

Printed in the United States of America

Phidippides Publications
4651 Roswell Road, Suite I-802
Atlanta, GA 30342 USA

TABLE OF CONTENTS

A short history of the Greek civilization that produced the Olympics, an extensive messenger system, and a victory in 490 BC. Phidippides probably ran 260 miles but was given credit for a very important 27. The first marathon race was only 25 miles, but the ancient messenger ran 26.

This is the program for those who want to enjoy the satisfaction of training for and participating in a long distance event yet have a real life. You'll learn the essential components of three days of training each week, a six-month training program that will work for almost anyone. All of the components are explained and coordinated to decrease the chance of injury and fatigue. The wall is the length of your longest training session in the last three weeks.

Whatever your goal, the long one will help you more than any component of your training program. By going slowly, you can burn more fat, push back your endurance barriers and go faster at shorter distance races.

Magic Mile. Performance Predictor. Reasons why you may not be improving.

Walk-running is what we were designed to do. How breaks extend capacity, erase fatigue, reduce injuries, restore resiliency, allow runners to improve time, speed recovery, and leave you feeling good enough to carry on social and family activities – even after the very long training sessions. Walk breaks were part of the marathon from the very first marathon race.

While virtually eliminating slowdown at the end, they keep the legs resilient. Mentally, they break up the event into segments which you know you can do. How long and how often to take breaks. My experience of improving from a 3:40 marathon without walk breaks to a 3:25 marathon with walk breaks.

Should I change my break ratio during the event? If I've never tried the walk breaks in training runs, would you advise taking them in the event? Are you saying that I can benefit from a break – even though I'm training for a sub-three hour marathon? Do I have to take walk/shuffle breaks at the end of my runs if my legs are tightening up? Do I need to take walk breaks on the short runs during the week? Walking question: How do I tell if I've been taking shuffle breaks often enough?

Walking correctly. What to avoid. What is a "shuffle?" No need to ever eliminate the breaks. How to use shuffle breaks.

First, get yourself into the habit of regular exercise, while you teach the muscles to burn fat. Next, finish your event. Then turn your attention to using running, walking and diet to burn fat if you want to.

Fat is potential energy, an unlimited supply of the very best fuel for running. Difference between men and women. How your "set point" is programmed to increase fat accumulation each year or so. Why diets don't work and how they set off the starvation reflex. My ice cream addiction.

How regular endurance exercise can move the set point down. Exercise gives you more control over your fat levels by burning up excess calories before they're deposited as fat and by training the muscle cells to burn more fat even when we're asleep. During the first 15 minutes of exercise, you burn glycogen, which produces a large waste product. From 15-45 minutes you transition into fat-burning. If you're still comfortably exercising after 45 minutes, you're in the fat-burning zone. How slow aerobic exercise with breaks burns more fat. Long training sessions are the best component for training your muscles to be fat-burners. How breaks affect calorie-burning. How to burn more fat by taking breaks. Why you don't want to lose a lot of weight and train for a long distance event at the same time.

The income side of the fat ledger. Eating all day long. Small meals energize; big meals put you to sleep. Mixing carbohydrates, fat, protein and fiber to feel good all day long. Eating an energy bar an hour before exercise can get you motivated. How to break up your daily food into small meals. How to manage blood sugar level. Complex carbohydrates give you a discount rate and a grace period. My list of lowfat foods that increase satisfaction. The reloading zone. Vitamins, minerals, alcohol, caffeine. Long-term nutritional health.

Counterattacking low blood sugar level on long ones. Blood sugar boosters. Choosing and testing energy food.

24 hours before and 24 hours after. Train your stomach. Eliminating problem foods. Eating countdown. Hyponatremia. Sports drinks. Follow the diet that got you here. Eating during the big event. Water vs. sports drinks. Some things to avoid.

You train yourself to be motivated. The left side of our brain tries to hold us back. The creative right brain. Fun, vision and focus. Why I run. The vision exercise. The difference between a dream and a vision. Transforming the vision into a mission. It starts with a date on a calendar. You must believe. Regularity.

Affirming the benefits of exercise. Confidence in the program. Be prepared to back up. The right group will motivate you. It could be low blood sugar. How to get out the door after a hard day at work. From the bed to the street.

Forward motion is motivating in itself. Get a mission and write it on the calendar. Don't go too fast. Bring the energy gel along. Be sure that you're not having a medical problem.

On the very tough or fast runs. Mantras for staying motivated. Getting beyond the mid-goal wall.

BREAKING THROUGH BARRIERS

Rehearse! Benefits of Rehearsal. Principles of mental rehearsal. The mental marathon, step-by-step. The battle: left brain vs. right brain. The night before. When the left brain bothers you. Wake up call. The line-up. The start. Challenges. Gutting it out. On to the finish.

Positive brainwashing. You can use my words: relax, power & glide. What happens when you say the magic words. Here's how to make your words magic. Achievement. I'm storing energy. Walking/Shuffling extends resources. No problems will get to me. Muscles—listen to me! I love hills! Short (stride) is better. I'm getting there.

It's time to play tricks on the left brain. Sneak down the road while the left brain is confused. One crazy thought can unlock another. The giant invisible rubber band. Oxygen molecules. Ball bearing atoms. A giant hand. Your inspiration shoes. The energy bar boost.

The post-race letdown. Select another mission before the big day. The body follows your mental vision. A few seconds of patience. Hydrate and avoid salt and alcohol. At the finish line. Throughout the afternoon. The next day. Two days after. Continue to alternate run or walk days with walk or shuffle days. Take one week off from racing and speed training for every six miles of the race. Weekend runs can gradually increase in distance. If you've done a half or full marathon and want to run another in the near future. The group will pull you through. The Marathon a Month club. Before and during, the little things which speed recovery.

THE BIG DAY: YOU STILL HAVE A CHANCE TO ASSUME CONTROL

You can still improve your performance during the last 48 hours. By being positive and staying focused, you assume most of the control over your attitude and your performance. Drink and avoid dehydrating elements. Eat small snacks regularly. Check out the staging area. Rest! Go slowly in the beginning and take your breaks. Eat during the second half of the event to keep up your blood sugar level—and your attitude. Above all, have fun!

General items. The night before. What to put in your marathon bag. Marathon morning list. Immediately afterward. Recovery routine.

inflammatory medications: see a doctor first. Treating injuries: get a doctor, don't stretch, stop activity, ice, compression, elevation, massage. Getting back to running.

Coming back from an injury. Sickness. Training interruptions of less than 14 days due to vacation, etc. Bring back the long one. Pacing the long ones. How quickly can you increase the length of the long one and get back into "half or full marathon range."

The top five reasons why you need shoe advice. If you can't find a running specialty store. Bring your worn shoes, socks, foot devices. You're in charge. Spend some time. Tell your shoe expert. Run in each shoe. First, look at function and then go for fit. Which works best on your feet when you run. The DON'Ts of shoe selection. Pronation. Over-pronation and Supination. Function: are you floppy or rigid? Shape: are you curved or straight? Be sure to lace your shoe securely around the ankle. Don't get locked into specific models or brands. When to buy another shoe.

How to run a half or full marathon efficiently. Posture, bounce and overstride. Correcting forward lean. Correcting overstride. Cadence drill. Troubleshooting form problems. Quads: too tired, sore or weak. Discomfort, pain or weakness behind the knee. Shoulder and neck muscles tired and tight. Hamstrings tired or sore. Knee pain. Sore feet and lower legs. Lower back tired and sore. Stretching warning.

The XT days on the schedule. XT can maintain conditioning while injured. The best exercise for running/walking. The best exercises for fat-burning. Beware of the stair! Gradually introduce the muscles to XT. How to ease into new exercises. If injured.

Water running helps healthy runners develop a smoother running motion while injured runners can stay in great shape. Water running form: running/walking motion, cross country ski motion, the sprint. Cautions.

Deep breathing is also called belly breathing. Eliminating side pains. Deep-breathing technique.

Stretching doesn't warm you up for a run.

Postural strength exercises. The crunch. Arm running. Here's how.

How to layer yourself when it's cold. Protect all skin and extremities. Warming up on very cold days. Why you don't want to sweat. Clothing thermometer: what to wear as it gets colder.

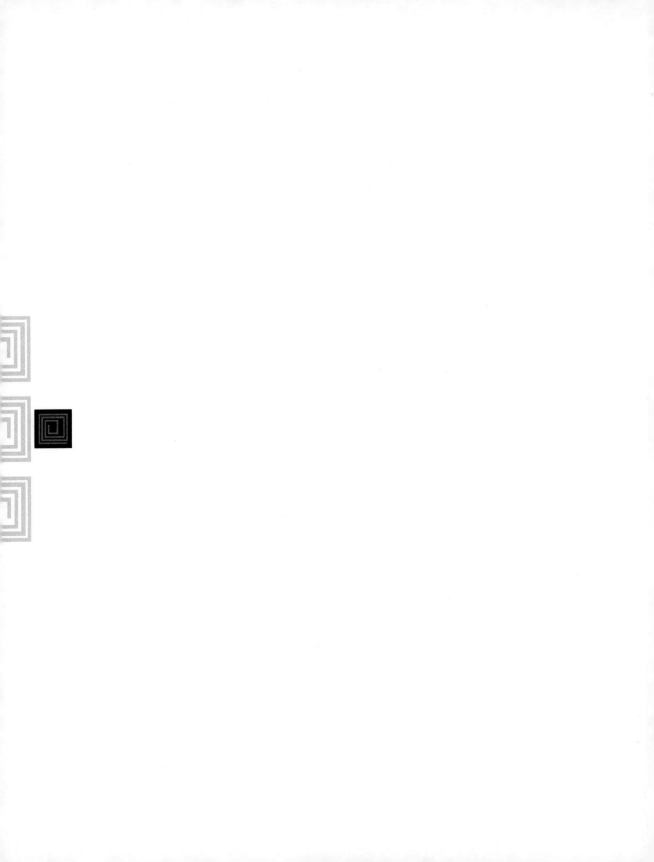

WHO IS JEFF GALLOWAY?

Coach to over 200,000 runners & walkers.

Jeff was an average high school runner who learned, trained hard and made the US Olympic team in 1972. His most satisfying moment, however, was pacing his teammate, Jack Bacheler, through the Olympic Trials Marathon and dropping back at the finish line so that Jack could take the final qualifying spot on the team. Since then, the force of his life has been helping others to enjoy the experience of running and the achievement of finishing a challenging event.

Jeff's experience includes being the first winner of the Peachtree Road Race in his hometown of Atlanta, GA and finishing over 130 marathons. His book, *Galloway's Book on Running* has been the best-selling running book over the past decade. Jeff's popular monthly column in *Runner's World* magazine is circulated to over two million each month.

Jeff's specialty is maximizing the enjoyment and satisfaction of running, while minimizing the time spent, the injuries and the fatigue. He keeps innovating and articulating techniques which help average people enjoy running more, run faster and reduce injuries.

In Jeff's training programs across North America, thousands of beginners finish a marathon six months after taking their first step. More important to Jeff is that most of these folks are hooked on fitness.

Jeff's family includes his wife of over 30 years, Barbara, and sons Westin and Brennan, all of whom are runners.

He conducts over 200 talks and seminars each year, receiving the direct feedback that keeps his articles and books focused on practical, helpful advice.

The feedback Jeff receives from his Ecoach clients, training program members, and Retreat and Running School participants provides the success base of the advice in this book.

Jeff still runs over 30 miles a week and hasn't had an overuse running injury in over 25 years.

DEDICATION

*D*onna Hicken started running in January of 1995 in hopes of burning off "baby fat" following the birth of her son Drew. The busy on-air TV news anchor had not been an exerciser before but "completely fell in love with it." Progressing through the distances of local road races, she finished the Gate River Run a year later and thought afterward that this 9.3 mile distance would be the longest she would ever want to run.

But in 1998 she got hooked on the marathon journey and the satisfaction of raising money for a charity. She finished the Walt Disney World Marathon but now admits that she was overtrained. She continued to try to push through nagging injuries until she heard the doctor say two ugly words, "stress fracture."

Donna was back in 1999, running the Boston Marathon on the Dana Farber Marathon Challenge team, raising funds for breast cancer research. "Ironically, seven months after that race, I became the cause. It was only the beginning of a very different kind of race for me."

In November of 1999, she was diagnosed with breast cancer. She struggled through major surgery, chemo and radiation. In 2002, when her life was beginning to normalize, there was more bad news: the cancer had returned. During the second round of surgery, chemo and radiation, when she said to herself "I just don't think I can do this anymore," she drew upon her experience as a runner.

"By that time I was well acquainted with 'the wall.' You know, that feeling somewhere around mile 20 in the marathon where you just want to sit in the road and cry. I knew that I could hit that wall and that if I just kept going, I could get to the other side. It gave me a level of confidence I wouldn't have had otherwise. I knew I'd be back and I knew I'd be running."

In 2003, she ran the Chicago Marathon to celebrate being cancer-free. That same year she founded the Donna Hicken Foundation. DHF pays for the critical needs of breast cancer patients while they are going through treatment. "Women shouldn't have to worry about how to pay rent and childcare when they are undergoing chemo."

In 2005, Donna and I met and decided to team up to train runners for the Jacksonville Marathon. This program (26.2 with Donna) enabled many beginning exercisers to finish a marathon six months later—even some who were being treated for breast cancer. Donna ran two marathons that year and believes that it was the Galloway program that kept her, and others, injury-free--while meeting new "friends for life."

"The most exciting news is that Jeff and I have decided to start our own marathon! It's the only marathon in the country dedicated to wiping out breast cancer in our lifetime and caring for women living with the disease right now. The *26.2 with Donna/ The National Marathon to Fight Breast Cancer* will certainly raise millions because 100 percent of the race entry fee is donated to breast cancer research/care. (Inaugural: February 17th of 2008 in Jacksonville Beach).

This book is dedicated to those who are changing their lives for the better by training for a significant endurance goal and for those who are raising funds to end cancer. Please join us in this important cause. *For more information on this event, visit www. breastcancermarathon.com.*

NOTE: Read Donna's chapter on page 173, "The Incredible Motivation in Running for Others"

BEFORE YOU TAKE
THOSE FIRST STEPS...

*T*here are very few people who should not exercise because of cardiovascular, structural, muscular or other problems. It is very important to ensure that you are not in this risk category.

• Before beginning any exercise, diet or other improvement program, be sure to have yourself and the program evaluated by specialists in the areas you are pursuing.

• The advice in this book is offered as such—advice from one exerciser to another. It is not meant to be a prescription and should be evaluated as noted above and below. Get help from medical authorities for medical issues.

• Specific structures and problems of individuals may require program modifications.

• In each area, find specialists who are also knowledgeable about the positive and other effects of exercise and running.

• Read the sections on Safety, Heart Issues and Heat.

• Never push through pain.

• Ask several respected leaders in the fitness community for recommendations of specialists.

• Always back off any exercise or program when you feel any risk of injury or health.

• The benefits come from regular exercise and steady adherence to a long-term program.

• Never radically increase the amount of exercise or drastically change diet and other health elements.

• Joining a group helps motivation.

• Have FUN and you'll want to continue.

You Can Do This!

*O*verwhelming is the best way to describe the floodtide of entrants into long distance events. Each year, beginning exercisers by the thousands are targeting a half or full marathon instead of the safer choice of a 5K or 10K. Established events are filling their quotas earlier than ever, and the overflow of procrastinators has been absorbed by a mushrooming growth of interesting regional and national events. What started as a once-in-a-lifetime achievement is now being renewed by former couch potatoes every six to 12 months,

At the same time that a majority of the North American population has been labeled "significantly overweight" or "obese," long distance training has been noted by many experts as the fastest growing activity in the field of exercise. Surely some of the two+ million who train for such events each year start with the goal of losing some of the blanket that has been accumulating around their midsections for a decade or so. The overwhelming number of those who continue, however, do so because of the unequaled positive attitude boost, significant stress release, and overall increase in vitality, focus and creativity.

As the average age of the runner/walker has increased to 40+, the half or full marathon has become the mid-life mission. It could be worse: when you list other mid-life diversions, this is not a bad choice. At this stage of life, a high percentage of these first-time exercisers are accustomed to relying upon key people and leveraging influence through contacts, income and other negotiable items. The half or full marathon stand out as two of the most esteemed of life's achievements, which have to be won by pulling from within oneself the physical, mental and spiritual resources over an extended period of time. The universal respect flows from sedentary observers who wish they could find the fortitude to get out there. Participants discover a mature self-respect, along with the previously dormant strengths and capabilities to meet the challenges on this six-month migration.

Part of the fulfillment must come from getting back to our roots. Our ancient ancestors walked and ran for thousands of miles each year to survive. In the process, they developed and passed on to us a treasury of physical and mental rewards, which we renew on every workout. The challenge of a significant physical journey on foot unleashes some primitive connections to our identity as human beings.

If you have read this far, chances are you're ready to go forward with one of most fulfilling experiences of your life. At the very least, you're saying that you want to take responsibility for your health and your attitude. On the long list of benefits from such a program, those two are at the top.

Every finisher, no matter how experienced, has to dig down and find resources to get through the training program and to the finish line. You'll discover unexpected strengths. Most of those on a mission become more positive and react more directly with life's offerings. As you view the finish banner and realize you're near the end of the journey, even the tough guys I let some tears loose.

Over the past four decades, my marathon count has exceeded 130. I've received the same wonderful exhilaration when running them fast (2:16) as when running them slowly. To reach the finish line in a half or full marathon is to enter a very elite group: about two tenths of one percent of the population. My most treasured marathon was my slowest. I ran with my father in the 1996 Boston Marathon in 5:59:48. He tells folks that if I hadn't been there to slow him down, he'd have run much faster.

To stick with a training program for six months is to become a winner.

To finish will leave you feeling like a champion and positively change your life.

You can do it!

VI

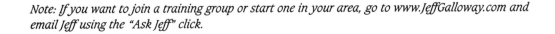

Note: If you want to join a training group or start one in your area, go to www.JeffGalloway.com and email Jeff using the "Ask Jeff" click.

PRODUCTS THAT ENHANCE RUNNING

*T*he following products will help almost all runners and walkers. For more information on these, visit www.JeffGalloway.com.

Other Galloway Books: training schedules and gifts that keep on giving— even to yourself (Order them, autographed, from www.JeffGalloway.com)

Walking: Walkers now have a book that explains the many benefits, how to maximize them, with training programs for 5K, 10K, Half and Full Marathons. There is resource information on fat-burning, nutrition, motivation and much more.

Getting Started: This is more than a state-of-the-art book for beginners. It gently takes walkers into running, with a 6-month schedule that has been very successful. Also included is information on fat-burning, nutrition, motivation and body management. This is a great gift for your friends or relatives who can be "infected" positively by running.

A Year-Round Plan You'll find daily workouts for 52 weeks for three levels of runners: to finish, to maximize potential and time improvement. It has the long runs, speed sessions, drills and hill sessions, all listed in the order needed to do a 5K, 10K, Half and Marathon during one year. Resource material is included to help with many running issues.

Galloway's Book On Running 2nd Edition: This is the best-seller among running books since 1984. Thoroughly revised and expanded in 2001, you'll find training programs for 5K, 10K, Half Marathon, with nutrition, fat-burning, walk breaks, motivation, injuries, shoes and much more. This is a total resource book.

Marathon This has the information you need to train for the classic event. There are training programs, with details on walk breaks, long runs, marathon nutrition, mental marathon toughness and much more.

Half Marathon This new book provides highly successful and detailed training schedules for various time goals for this important running goal. Information is provided on nutrition, mental preparation, fluids, race day logistics & checklist, and much more.

Testing Yourself: Training programs for 1 mile, 2 miles, 5K, and 1.5 miles are detailed, along with information on racing-specific information in nutrition, mental toughness, running form. There are also some very accurate prediction tests that allow you to tell what is a realistic goal. This book has been used effectively by those who are stuck in a performance rut at 10K or longer events. By training and racing faster, you can improve running efficiency and your tolerance for waste products, like lactic acid.

Running Until You're 100 In the chapter on joint health, you'll see in the research studies that runners have healthier joints than sedentary folks. In the chapter on the researched health benefits of exercise, an expert on longevity says that for every hour we exercise we can expect to get back 2 hours of life extension. Among the heroes section is an 85-year-old who recently finished his 700th marathon and will do 29 more this year. There are nutrition suggestions from Nancy Clark, training adjustments by decade and many other helpful hints for running past the century mark.

VIII *Fit Kids—Smarter Kids* This book is a handbook for parents, teachers and youth leaders in how to lead kids into fitness that is fun. A growing number of studies are listed that document how kids who exercise do better in academics and in life. Nancy Clark gives tips on what to eat, and there's a chapter on childhood obesity—with the hope that others, like the author (a former fat kid), can turn things around. There are resources, successful programs, inspirational stories and much more.

A Woman's Guide To Running by Barbara and Jeff Galloway. This book covers the many women-specific exercise issues not seen in many books: menstrual periods, pregnancy, menopause, osteoporosis, PMS, choosing a bra, chaffing, etc. You'll find state-of-the-art fat-burning information, practical eating, aches and pains, nutrition by Nancy Clark, motivation training and much more.

A Woman's Guide to Walking (Due in July 2007) This is the walkers' version of the above guide for runners.

Running Schools and Retreats: Jeff conducts motivating running schools and retreats. These feature individualized information, form evaluation, comprehensively covering running, nutrition and fat-burning.

Podfitness—coaching through the ipod

As an extension of his training programs, Jeff has teamed up with Podfitness.com to bring these workouts into your daily life. Now, you can have a custom program, during which Jeff coaches you through every training session on your iPod.

"My Podfitness training program is designed to reinforce what you've read here. Your program is designed expressly for you and changes with you. You'll hear me throughout your workout, offering advice and encouragement. Plus, it lays your music in the background, which I think makes each run even more enjoyable."

"Go to http://www.podfitness.com/jeffgalloway/ and they'll let you try it for free. I'm positive you'll be as impressed with it as I was and that you'll become a better runner for it." JG

Foam Roller—self massage for I-T Band, Hip, etc.

This cylinder of dense foam is about six inches in diameter and about one foot long. We've not seen any mode of treatment for Ilio-tibial band injury that has been more effective. For best effect, put the roller on the floor, and lie on your side so that the irritated I-T band area is on top of the roller. As your body weight presses down on the roller, roll up and down on the area of the leg you want to treat. Roll gently for two to three minutes and then apply more pressure as desired. This is actually a deep tissue massage that you can perform on yourself. For I-T band, we recommend rolling it before and after running. See www.RunInjury-Free.com for more info on this product.

Cryo-Cup—best tool for ice massage

Rubbing with a chunk of ice on a sore area (when near the skin) is very powerful therapy. We know of hundreds of cases of Achilles tendon problems that have been healed by this method. The Cryo-Cup is a very convenient device for ice massage. The plastic cup has a plastic ring that sits on top of it. Fill it up with water, then freeze. When you have an ache or pain that is close to the skin, take the product out of the freezer, pour warm water over the outside of the cup to release it and hold onto the plastic handle like an ice "popsicle." Rub constantly up and down the affected area for about 15 minutes, until the area is numb. When finished, fill the cup and place in the freezer. In my experience, rubbing with a plastic bag of ice—or a frozen gel product—does no good at all in most cases.

YOU CAN DO IT—motivational audio CD

Put this in your car player as you drive to your run. You'll be motivated by the stories as you learn the strategies and methods that have allowed runners to deal with the negative messages of the left side of the brain—and push to their potential.

Endurox Excel (discount available at www.JeffGalloway.com)

Many runners over 50 years old have told us that they have noticed a significantly faster muscle rebound when using this product. An hour before a long or hard workout, Jeff takes two of these Excel pills. Among the anti-oxidants is the active ingredient from gensing: ciwega. Research has shown that recovery time is reduced when this product is taken. We also use it when our legs have been more tired than usual for two to three days in a row.

Accelerade (discount available at www.JeffGalloway.com)

This sports drink has a patented formula shown to improve recovery. Drinking it before and after prolonged, dehydrating workouts also helps to improve hydration. We recommend having a half gallon container of Accelerade in the refrigerator. Drink four to eight ounces every one to two hours, throughout the day. Best time to "top off" your fluid levels is within 24 hours before a long run. Prime time for replacing fluids is during the 24 hour period after a long run. Many runners have 32 oz or so in a thermos, for sipping during walk breaks in a prolonged speed training session. I suggest adding about 25 percent more water than recommended.

Research has also shown that drinking Accelerade about 30 minutes before running can get the body's startup fuel (glycogen) activated more effectively and may conserve the limited supply of this crucial fuel.

Endurox R4 (discount available at www.JeffGalloway.com)

This product has almost "cult following" status among runners. In fact, the research shows that the 4:1 ratio of carbohydrate to protein helps to reload the muscle glycogen more quickly (when consumed within 30 minutes of the finish of a hard or long workout. This means that the muscles feel bouncy and ready to do what you can do, sooner. There are other anti-oxidants in R4 that speed recovery.

IX

Jeff Galloway's Training Journal

Some type of journal is recommended to organize, and track, your training plan. *Jeff Galloway's Training Journal* can be ordered from www.JeffGalloway.com, autographed. It simplifies the process, with places to fill in information for each day. There is also space for recording the unexpected thoughts and experiences that make so many runs come alive again as we read them.

Your journal allows you to take control over the organization of your training components. As you plan ahead and then compare notes afterward, you are empowered to learn from your experience and make positive changes.

Galloway PC Coach—interactive software This software will not only set up a marathon training program, it will help you to stay on track. As you log in, you're told if your training is not what it should be for that day. Sort through various training components quickly and often find reasons why you are tired or have more aches and pains, etc.

Vitamins (discount available at www.Jeff Galloway.com)

I now believe that most runners need a good vitamin to boost the immune system and resist infection. There is some evidence that getting the proper vitamin mix can also speed recovery. The vitamin line I use is called Cooper Complete. Dr. Kenneth Cooper (founder of the Cooper Clinic and the Aerobics Institute), is behind this product. In the process of compiling the most formidable body of research on exercise and long-term health I've seen anywhere, he found that certain vitamins play important roles.

Javette

Caffeine is scientifically proven to enhance performance during exercise, especially in running. I drink coffee every day & fully understand its benefits. Javette provides just the right amount of caffeine in a tasty & convenient way. Javette's the coffee for convenient caffeine!

Buffered Salt Tablets—to reduce cramping

If your muscles cramp on long or hard runs, due to salt depletion, this type of product may help greatly. The buffered sodium and potassium tablets get into the system more quickly. Be sure to ask your doctor if this product is okay for you (those with high blood pressure, especially). If you are taking a statin drug for cholesterol, and are cramping, it is doubtful that this will help. Ask your doctor about adjusting the medication before long runs.

Control over pace by GPS and other distance-pace calculators

There are two types of devices for measuring distance, and both are usually very accurate: GPS and accelerometer technology. While some devices are more accurate than others, most will tell you, almost exactly how far you have run/walked. These will allow you to gain control over your pace—from the first tenth of a mile.

Freedom! With these devices, you can run/walk your long ones wherever you wish, instead of having to repeat a loop—just because it is measured. Instead of going to a track to do a "magic mile," you can very quickly measure your segments on roads, trails or residential streets.

The GPS devices track your movements by the use of navigational satellites. In general, the more satellites, the more accurate the measurement. There are "shadows" where the signals cannot be acquired: buildings, forests or mountains. On trails with lots of small turns, the device may cut the tangents as it accounts for the mileage. These are usually temporary interruptions but will tend to give a mileage reading that is less that the distance you actually ran/walked.

The accelerometer products require a very easy calibration and have been shown to be very accurate. The "chip" on your shoe is very sensitive to movement and effort and sends the data to the wrist monitor. I've not heard of any pattern of technical interference with this technology. I've found it best during the calibration, to use a variety of paces, taking a walk/shuffle break or two in order to simulate what you will be doing when you run/walk.

Some devices require batteries, and others can be re-charged. Experienced staff members at a technical running store can often advise you on the pros and cons of each product. Sometimes they'll also share the "gossip" on the various brands and models, gained from the feedback they receive from customers.

XI

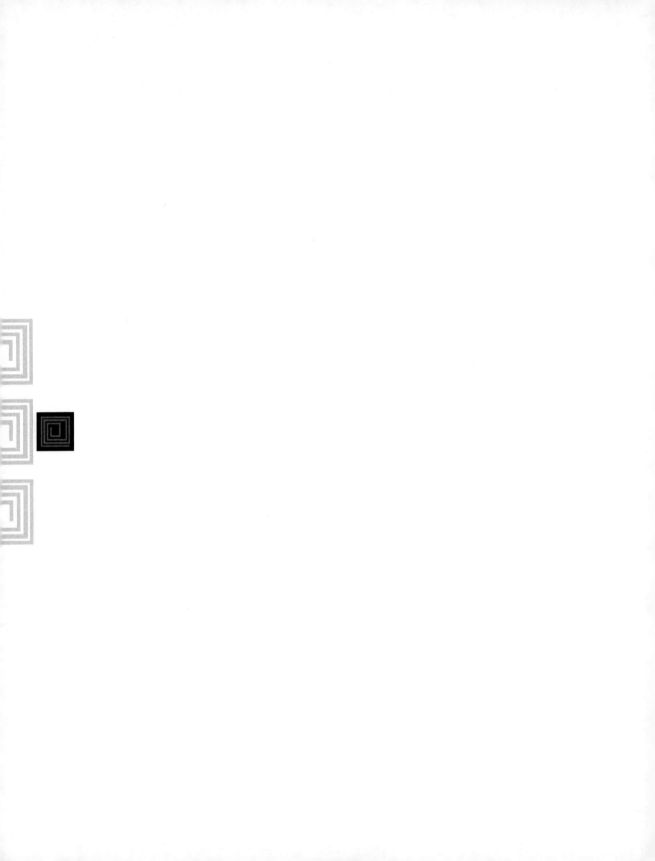

WHERE DID THE
MARATHON COME FROM?

*T*hat's simple. In the first modern Olympics, in 1896, there was a race to commemorate the trek of the ancient messenger from the plain of Marathon to Athens to report a great Greek victory in 490 BC. But like so many supposedly simple historical facts, this one has many plots and subplots.

Ancient Greek Olympians ran short distance races in stadiums. I have the good fortune to regularly take groups of runners and walkers to visit these sites in Greece. Chillbumps pop up every time I visit and jog down the field. You can put your feet in the grooves of the starting blocks they used and experience a direct connection to the vitality of the ancient Olympic concept. This will keep you motivated to get out the door for weeks or months on your return home!

But there were excellent long distance runners in ancient Greece who never competed but provided fast communication links throughout that civilization. Often logging more than a marathon a day, these endurance specialists could navigate the tricky Greek terrain, covering very long distances faster than horses. They were expected to not only deliver the news but to also interpret it, emphasize key points, and return with a reply, including a description of the facial expression and emotion of the respondent.

Phidippides rose to the challenge in 490 BC. As a messenger for the Athenian army, he and the other soldiers assembled on the hills above the plain of Marathon, hoping to confront the aggressive and militaristic Persians, who had just invaded Greek soil and set up camp 25 miles from Athens. The enemy had a numerical advantage of about five to one.

This was a crucial period in the development of the democratic experiment in Athens. Contrary to the more autocratic governments of the other great civilizations to that point, the Athenians encouraged individual freedoms and personal growth and achievement. The epitome of this philosophy was the Olympic games, which elevated fitness and sport to a level of respect equal to valued professions. Indeed, the Greeks recorded history according to the four-year Olympiad in which the event occurred. The Persians were determined to snuff out these radical ideas.

The Athenian generals knew that this was a winner-take-all situation. If they lost, the Persians would kill them, burn Athens and enslave their families. The residents of Athens already had a plan to burn the city in order to deprive the Persians of some of their spoils.

The historical record of this period was passed down in oral reports and written down more than two centuries later by Herodotus and others. While the storytelling method of Greek history has been shown to be generally accurate through research and excavation, names and details sometimes became blurred.

Phidippides was mentioned several times in the accounts of the 490 BC campaign. When the committee of three generals who commanded the Athenians looked over the massive beachhead of their opponents, they wisely decided to ask for help, sending a messenger to Sparta. Whereas the Spartans governed by a different philosophy, they certainly would benefit from an Athenian victory; without it, the Persians would be headed their way.

The messenger sent to Sparta (about 130 miles away) was probably Phidippides. A day and a half later he arrived and went before the Spartan rulers to plead for their help. Relatively quickly, they gave him the good news that Sparta would send troops. Unfortunately, they were in the middle of a community ritual and couldn't come for about 10 days.

Another day and a half later, Phidippides had run back to the hills above Marathon and reported to the leadership. Realizing that the Persians wouldn't wait 10 days to attack, they devised an innovative battle plan and attacked with a thin front line. The Persians quickly broke through, thought they had won, and started celebrating. Suddenly the best Greek soldiers hit them from both sides, inflicting massive casualties. Having lost their focus and probably suspecting a supernatural force, the Persians ran for their ships and sailed away. One of the great battles of western civilization had been won.

Historical accounts tell us that a soldier/messenger was then dispatched to Athens

to tell of the victory before the Athenians burned their city. Tradition has bestowed the honor of making that "victory lap" upon Phidippides. He covered the long gradual uphill, followed by a gradual downhill into the city and said the unexpected but exhilarating word to the fragile democracy: "Nike" (victory). Athens would live but the wounded and exhausted messenger died.

When the organizers were deciding which events to include in the first modern Olympic games (Athens, 1896), a friend of the prime organizer, De Courbetin, suggested that the run of Phidippides be commemorated in a footrace from the plain of Marathon to the Olympic Stadium. The marathon was born and reporters noted that all of the original competitors walked and ran in that first race. The marathon is one of two events which has been run in every one of the modern Olympic games.

The distance from the tomb at the battlefield to the 1896 stadium is 25 miles, which continued as the official distance until the London Olympics in 1908. The 25-mile course had been measured and marked when the Queen asked if she might be able to watch the start from the palace. The course was extended by 1.2 miles to accommodate the royal request, and the new distance became official. A few years ago, however, as I was walking from the 1896 stadium towards the ancient site of Athens, I realized that Phidippides would have run about 26 miles: the ancient town of Athens is about a mile further down the road from where the 1896 Olympic marathon ended.

A tradition among veteran marathoners when passing the original finish distance at 25 miles is to say "God save the Queen" or something like that. But considering Phidippides' run for reinforcements to Sparta and back, today's marathoners are getting off easy—we could be running 260 miles.

SETTING UP *YOUR* TRAINING PROGRAM

1. The long one gradually increases to 13 or 26 miles and gives you the specific endurance needed to complete the 10-miler, half or full marathon.

2. To maintain this endurance, the weekly minimum is 60 minutes of running, walking or walk-running, divided between two to five days.

3. Slower is better on the long ones: the slower you go, the faster you will recover, while receiving all of the endurance.

4. Frequent walk/shuffle breaks, from the beginning of each long one, add fun and reduce fatigue dramatically.

5. There are almost no injuries among those who adhere to this minimum program.

6. Those who have finished a 10-miler, half or full marathon can train for a faster one by doing speed sessions on non-long weekends.

THE THREE-DAY-A-WEEK PROGRAM
Goal: To Finish

Mon	Tue	Wed	Thu	Fri	Sat	Sun
off or walk 30-60 minutes	run/walk 30 minutes	off or walk 30-60 minutes	run/walk 30 minutes	off or walk 30-60 minutes	off	long run/walk

ALMOST ANYONE CAN COMPLETE A HALF OR FULL MARATHON IN SIX MONTHS!

Even if you only have 60 minutes to exercise during the work week, you can train for the half or full marathon. The minimum is actually better for reducing injuries. During the week, you only need to accumulate an hour of running/walking. The long run/walk starts at three miles and gradually increases by one mile each week until it reaches 10 miles. Then, you'll do the long one every other week, with a run/walk of half the distance on the "off" weekend. After half or full marathoners complete the nine-miler (half)/18-miler (full), they'll receive two easy weekends for good behavior, shifting to a long one every third week.

WEEKEND ENDURANCE + 60 MINUTES OF MAINTENANCE + REST

Your body is designed to continuously improve its endurance if you gently stress it in a pattern of increases, rest enough for rebuilding and do regular maintenance so that it won't forget the process. Think of your training program as a sound system. Each exercise session serves as a component designed to produce a specific effect. The long run provides the gentle challenge through mileage extension, which will develop the exact endurance necessary for getting to the finish line. The slow and minimal 60 minutes of maintenance run/walks during the week simply maintain the conditioning gained on the weekend. Resting the running/walking muscles on other days is crucial for letting the muscles rebuild, dur-

> ## *Y*ou can't go too slowly on a long one.

ing which they make marvelous adaptations for easier and longer training.

THE LONG ONE BUILDS ENDURANCE

As you extend a mile or so farther on each long one, you push back your endurance limit. It is important to go slowly on each of these (at least two minutes per mile slower than you could go that distance on that day) to make it easy for your muscles to extend their current endurance limit and recover afterward. As you lengthen the long one to 13 or 26 miles, you build the exact endurance necessary to complete the half or full marathon. Walk/shuffle breaks, taken from the beginning (see section below) will also speed your recovery and make the extra distance on each run a gentle challenge. *Note: Walkers should walk very gently.*

On the non-long weekends, there are several options. Most will do a slow run/walk of about half the distance of the current long one (up to 7 miles). On two to four of these "easy" weekends, it is wise to do a "magic mile" time trial to predict what you might be able to do. *(See the Predicting Race Performance page in the Practical Advice section of this book.)* Veterans who want to improve will do speed sessions on some of the non-long weekends. If you're feeling good during these shorter ones, runners can do them continuously, but there's no advantage in doing this. In other words, walk breaks are at your discretion on the shorter runs, including the ones during the week. *Note: Walkers should use a short stride.*

LONG RUN/WALK FACTS:

♦ Twenty miles with walking breaks (or shuffle breaks) equals 20 miles run continuously... at any speed (but you recover faster with walk breaks).

♦ Forget about speed on the long ones. Focus only on the component of endurance.

♦ You can't run/walk too slowly on the long ones. Go at least two minutes per mile slower than you could run that distance on that day, accounting for heat, humidity, etc. *Note: Walkers should walk very comfortably.*

♦ You won't usually feel bad when you're walking/running too fast at the beginning so you must force yourself to slow down.

♦ The day before the long one should be a no-exercise day.

WALK BREAKS OR SHUFFLE BREAKS ON LONG ONES

♦ Must be taken early and often to reduce pounding and fatigue

♦ Must be taken often to allow the primary running/walking muscles to recover fast—even when increasing length

♦ Will also help most to run/walk faster in the marathon itself

Note: Runners must still slow down the overall pace to at least two minutes per mile slower than the "magic mile" predicted pace.

The most important breaks are the ones taken during the first mile and the second most important set, those taken in the second mile. etc. When taken from the beginning of all long ones, walk/shuffle breaks erase fatigue, speed recovery, reduce injury, and yet bestow all of the endurance of the distance covered. In other words, a slow long run/walk with walk/shuffle breaks gives you the same distance conditioning

> **"*T* wo-Minute Rule" for runners: On long runs, you must run at least two minutes per mile slower than you could run that distance on that day (accounting for heat, humidity, hills, etc.).**

as a fast one, when both cover the same distance.

Everyone should take a one-minute walk/shuffle break every one to six minutes on every long one. If you're just beginning to run, you'll walk more than you'll run. Experienced marathoners will recover much faster from their long ones when they take one-minute walk breaks at least every six minutes. *(See the Run-Walk-Run chapter for more details. Runners and walkers should pay special attention to the Walk/Shuffle Break section.)*

DOING "THE MINIMUM" WILL DECREASE YOUR CHANCE OF INJURY AND FATIGUE

The bad news: When you extend your endurance limits on each long one, you'll stress and break down the muscle and energy systems. The good news comes after rest days. When you give the running/walking muscles a chance to recover, they make dozens of adaptations, gearing you up for an even greater challenge one to three weeks later. If you're not getting enough rest, your muscles will accumulate pockets of microtears, which will continue to accumulate until you experience extreme fatigue or injury.

Tens of thousands of average people have gone through our program, with almost no injuries among those who follow the minimum. There are always some, however, who have to push the envelope. The few who get injured in our training groups are almost always those who add distance, speed or exercise days to our recommended schedule.

Because this is a bare-bones program, it's very important to do every one of the sessions during the week to maintain long run endurance. You can run/walk these in 10-minute segments, accumulating the magic hour of exercise over a four to five-day period. As is true with "cramming" before exams, it's not effective to get in all 60 minutes during the two days before the next long one. The day before these treks should be devoid of exercise—or at least no exercise for the calf muscles in the lower leg.

REST AND CROSS TRAINING

Significant rest is as important as the stress components of the program. It's actually during the rest days that your muscles rebuild stronger and make adaptations for greater efficiency. Only if you back off enough from the stress will the muscles recover enough to prevent injury or lingering tiredness.

Avoid exercises such as stair machines, leg strength exercise, cycling that involves standing up and step aerobics classes. The most common cross training exercises are walking, swimming, cycling, upper body strength exercise and water running.

Cross training won't improve your time, and it's not necessary for finishing. It will provide attitude-boosting endorphins, stress release, and fat-burning on the days when you need to let your running/walking muscles recover. *(For more information, consult the chapter on Cross Training in this book.)*

SPEED

Only those who have completed a half or full marathon before should even consider a time goal. The primary benefit in this program comes from covering the gradually increasing distance of the long run/walk. After having run over 60 marathons for time and over 70 just to finish, I believe that time improvement is for the ego, but there's noth-

5

*Y*es, it's possible to train for a long distance event and have a life.

ing wrong with that. The speed game can be interesting, but most of the satisfaction comes from crossing the finish line. The first half or full marathon should be done at a slow enough pace so that you reach the finish line knowing that you could run faster and that you want to run another.

Veterans who have finished at least one half or full marathon and want to improve their times can add a speed component on some of the non-long weekends. You'll find my recommended schedule of hill play and then mile repeats listed in the training schedules and in the Speedplay chapter in this book. Please be careful because the addition of speed will increase your chance of injury. As long as your goal is realistic, you're taking sufficient rest, and you adapt the speedwork pace to weather conditions, you'll give the body the creative stress it needs to help you improve in a series of steps. Don't add to the program, and monitor your "weak links" to minimize the chance of overstress and injury.

6

Veterans will increase their chance of time goal fulfillment by increasing the length of the long one beyond race distance. This builds extra endurance, which gives your legs the capacity to keep pushing during the latter stages of the race. On these extra long ones, the recommended pace reduction from the beginning is at least two and a half minutes per mile slower than you could run that distance on that day.

BEWARE OF MIXING COMPONENTS

Running/walking too fast on the long one will leave you much more tired, with multiples of damaged muscle cells, than you've experienced by following the Two-Minute Rule. Not only does this increase the chance of injury, but veterans who try to put speed into the long one will sacrifice the quantity or quality of their speedplay later in the week. Often this fatigue is so subtle that you don't feel it for two or three long ones, due to the release of stress hormones, which mask the sensations of tiredness.

CAUTIONS FOR TIME GOAL RUNNERS

Running too long or too fast during speed-play sessions will reduce the prospective benefit. Speed in endurance events is developed, like endurance, in a series of many speed sessions, each pushing only a little further than the one before. Going further or faster than you have been in the recent past will increase recovery time and complicate the rebuilding process. When too many of the muscle cells are damaged, the muscle doesn't rebuild stronger for a long time.

Maintenance runs that are too fast will slow down recovery and increase the buildup of fatigue. It is important that your 60 minutes of maintenance exercise during the week is done slowly enough so the muscles will recover from the previous weekend. When in doubt, go slower.

IT HELPS TO HAVE A GROUP

One of the most delightful things I do is help set up training groups around North America. Each group member finds a significant motivation boost to do the long ones and to get in the 60 minutes during the week. You'll be inspired by your "team-mates" some days, and you'll inspire them on others. Choose a team that has the same fitness condition as you. The goal is to go slowly enough on long ones that even the least conditioned members of the group can keep up. In each of the cities where we have groups, we have several sub-groups, based upon fitness level.

*Y*es, it's possible to complete every long one, even a 26-miler, without hitting the couch or bed all afternoon and evening.

WHERE IS *THE WALL*?

Most marathoners/half marathoners who start their long ones too fast or exceed the length of their current long one by more than three miles or both will experience a fatigue "wall" at the end of the run/walk. If you're going within your capabilities from the beginning, you'll be tired as you reach the mileage of your longest one in the past two to three weeks. Most can go one to two miles beyond that point, accumulating more fatigue quickly but able to move ahead as before. The wall hits you quickly as you reach your limits. Within a few yards, you go from feeling tired but capable of continuing forward to feeling like you can't go more than a few steps. The muscles have gone too far beyond their limit and can't handle it any more. Because of the physical stress, your left brain sends you streams of negative messages which tell you to quit, question your sanity and ask you philosophical questions such as: "Why are you doing this?"

So your wall is normally the length of your longest endurance session within the last two to three weeks, provided you are going at the pace you could on that day. Even a little too fast in the beginning will introduce you to the wall sooner. On a hot, humid day, you'll bump into that wall before you should—if you don't slow your pace down even more than normal from the beginning. Even those who have missed a long one in the marathon schedule have been able to do the next long one by slowing down to at least three minutes per mile slower than they could run and by taking walk breaks much more frequently. The more conservative you are, in pace and in walking, from the beginning of the run, the more you can push your wall back farther and farther with little risk of fatigue or injury.

WHY DO I NEED A 14-MILE TRAINING SESSION BEFORE THE HALF MARATHON OR A 26-MILE TRAINING SESSION BEFORE THE FULL MARATHON?

I get a lot of feedback on this one. My name is used in vain, they tell me, during the 14 and the 26 milers. But within 24 hours, the wonderful realization and confidence takes hold: "I've gone the distance."

On each long one, including the 14/26-miler, most who are training for their first one are going farther than they have ever gone in their lives, by two to three miles. After finishing the final workout, the training is complete. You won't have to push your wall back during the race itself. You have arrived.

The confidence bestowed by that last long one will take away many of the nervous anxieties leading up to the race itself. You're going to have some negative messages from that left side of the brain anytime you attempt a challenge like this. You'll reduce them down to a manageable level after the completion of this, the ultimate long training session.

I'VE HEARD THAT GOING BEYOND 20 MILES BREAKS YOU DOWN

Only if you go too fast. Impatient runners and "type A" running personalities have spread the breakdown rumors after running too fast on a long one. They are so tired after an 18 to 20-mile run that they can't imagine how anyone could run longer than that without dire consequences. When long runs become races, the body accumulates fatigue, which may not be erased by event day.

7

> **Y**es, it's possible to finish a half or full marathon and celebrate with friends and family that evening.

It's an entirely different story when you go at a pace at least two minutes per mile slower than you could go on that day - and take the walk breaks which you need. On each long one you gently push your endurance barrier back another two to three miles. Gentle fatigue, yes; breakdown, no. Tens of thousands of half or full marathoners have pushed their walls back gently without breaking down. You can too!

HOW DO I KNOW IF I'M GOING TWO MINUTES PER MILE SLOWER THAN I COULD RUN ON THAT DAY?

The **"huff and puff"** rule will help walkers set pace: If you're huffing and puffing so much during the last two to three miles of a long one that you can't carry on a conversation, you went too fast from the beginning of that workout. On the next one, significantly slow down, take shuffle breaks more frequently or both. Remember to write a note to yourself, which you'll read just before starting your next long one. *(See the section on Predicting Race Performance and Training Pace.)*

BUT I HAVE A TIME GOAL, EVEN IF IT'S MY FIRST ONE...

A time goal puts stress on you before and during the first half or full marathon, which will reduce your enjoyment of the big moment. By backing off by two minutes per mile slower than you could go that distance on that day, you'll be able to enjoy the course, talk to your fellow runners and walkers and share the experience. You'll cross that finish line knowing that you could go faster, and this will motivate you to do just that...if you want to.

I ran my first 60 marathons hard. Now I've run more than 70 running within myself. I have received the same satisfaction, sense of achievement and internal glow from all of the slow ones as I did from the fast ones. The main difference is that I could appreciate the satisfaction and celebrate the achievement on the slow ones. I wasn't very social for very long after the fast ones.

DOESN'T SLOW RUNNING/ WALKING PRODUCE A SLOW RUNNER/WALKER?

Actually, doing a fast long training workout will produce an even slower runner/walker—one with dead legs that don't recover between long ones. There is only one purpose of the long one: to build endurance. The most effective way to do this is to slowly cover two to three miles further than you went on your previous long one. The slower you go, the more quickly you'll recover so that you can do the speed you need to get faster. *(See the section on Speedplay, which will produce a faster runner.)*

WHAT TYPE OF MEDICAL CLEARANCE DO I NEED?

Before you start a strenuous training program, be sure to get clearance from a doctor who knows the benefits of exercise. The chance is tiny that you'll have a problem that will prevent you from continuing, but let's make sure.

8

THE LONG ONE

*W*hatever your goal, the long one will help you more than any component of your training program. By going slowly, you can burn more fat, push back your endurance barriers and go faster at shorter distance races.

WHAT IS A LONG ONE?

The long one starts with the longest distance you've covered within the last two weeks and increases by one mile on a weekly long one up to five miles for the half and 10 miles for the full. At that point, you'll shift to going long every other weekend, increasing by two miles each time.

THE MENTAL BENEFITS

While there are significant and continuing physical benefits from going farther regularly, the mental ones are greater. Each week, I hear from beginners after they have just gone farther than they have ever gone. This produces mental momentum, self-confidence and a positive attitude. By slowing the pace and taking walk/shuffle breaks, you can also experience a series of victories over fatigue with almost no risk of injury.

PUSHING BACK YOUR LIMITS

As you push a mile or three farther on each long one, you push back your endurance limit. It's important to go slowly on each of these (at least two minutes per mile slower than you could cover that distance on that day) to make it easy for your muscles to extend their current endurance limit.

THE MOST DIRECT WAY TO PREPARE FOR THE MARATHON

As you extend the long one to 26/14 miles, you build the exact endurance necessary to complete the marathon (14 to 15 for the half marathon, 8 to 10 for the 10K). Those who have time goals can extend their capacity by running as far as 17 miles (half) and 30 miles (full) three to four weeks before the event. You're actually pushing back your "endurance wall" with each long one.

WALK BREAKS SPEED RECOVERY

Walk breaks, taken from the beginning, will also speed your recovery and make the extra distance on each one nothing more than a gentle challenge. *(See the section on Walk/Shuffle Breaks.)*

AS THE LONG ONES GET LONGER...

- Slow down the pace, from the beginning, by going at least two minutes per mile slower than you could on that day.

- Increase the frequency of walk/shuffle breaks. *(See the Run-Walk-Run chapter.)*

Signs that you went too fast on a long one:

- You must hit the couch or bed and rest for an hour or more

- Muscle soreness or leg fatigue which lasts for more than two days, making it uncomfortable to run/walk

- Aches and/or pains that last for more than four days after a long one

- Huffing and puffing so much during the last two to three miles that you can't carry on a conversation

- Struggling during the last two to three miles to maintain pace or slowing down

- An increase in nausea and irritation at the end

RUNNERS: PACING OF LONG ONES AND THE THE TWO-MINUTE RULE

Run all of the long ones at least two minutes per mile slower than event pace predicted by the "magic mile." The walk breaks will help you to slow the pace, but you must go slower as well. You get the same endurance from the long one if you go slowly as you would if you went fast. However, you'll recover much faster from a slow long workout. *(See the next chapter on specific pace predictions.)*

An additional slowdown should be made for increased temperature: 30 sec per mile slower for each 5 degrees of temperature increase above 60° F.

NON-LONG WEEKENDS

On the non-long weekends, you have several options. Most runners/walkers will do a slow run/walk of about half the distance of the current long one. On two to four of these "easy" weekends, it's wise to do a "magic mile" to predict what you might be able to do in the event. Veterans may do speed sessions on some of the non-long week-ends. If you're feeling good on these shorter workouts, you can leave out the walk/shuffle breaks, but there's no advantage in doing this. In other words, the breaks are at your discretion on the shorter distances, including the ones during the week.

ALMOST EVERYONE HAS AT LEAST ONE "BAD" LONG ONE

You may never be able to discover why, but if you know, learn! The tough ones teach you that you have hidden inner strengths, which you can draw upon on future challenges, both in training and in life itself. This will particularly help your confidence and your ability to withstand adversity in the race itself.

FLUID INTAKE

According to the medical teams of the major marathons, the recommended fluid intake during long ones and the half or full marathon itself, is 14 to 27 oz an hour. This is about four ounces, every one to two miles.

You get more of your money's worth on a slow long one—you get to experience it longer.

Long run facts:

- Twenty miles with walk/shuffle breaks equals 20 miles at the same pace (but you recover faster with breaks).

- Forget about speed on long ones. Focus only on the component of endurance.

- You can't go too slowly on the long ones.

- You won't usually feel bad when you're going too fast at the beginning. You must force yourself to slow down.

- The day before the long one should be a no-exercise day.

11

CHOOSING THE RIGHT
GOAL...AND PACE
FOR RUNNERS

*I*n this chapter you'll learn how to gain control over your pacing and how to determine the right pace for you on long runs and in your race. Veterans will learn how much improvement can be expected and whether they are on track for the goal at various times in the training program. As you approach your goal at the end of the program, you can use the "Galloway Performance Predictor" to determine what is realistic in your race—and how to make adjustments for temperature.

PREDICTION STRATEGY

About 1995, I started using a one-mile time trial (called a "magic mile") as a prediction tool. After working with hundreds and then thousands of runners, I've found that those who do three to four of these during a season can get a very realistic prediction of their current racing potential. By adding two min/mi to this time, runners will find an injury-reducing pace for the long runs.

The "magic mile" time trial (MM)

1. Go to a track or other accurately measured course. One mile is 4 laps around a track.

2. Warm up by walking for 5 minutes, then running a minute and walking a minute for 6-10 minutes and then jogging an easy 800-meter (half mile or two laps around a track).

3. Do 4 acceleration-gliders. These are listed in the "Drills" chapter.

4. Walk for 3-4 minutes.

5. Run fast—for you—for 4 laps. Use walk break suggestions in this chapter or run the way you want.

6. On your first time trial, don't run all-out from the start—just a little faster than you have been running.

7. Warm down by reversing the warmup.

8. A school track is the best venue. Don't use a treadmill because they tend to be notoriously un-calibrated and often tell you that you ran farther or faster than you really did.

9. On each successive test, try to adjust your pace in order to run a faster time than you've run before.

10. Use the "Galloway Prediction Formula" below to see what time is predicted in the goal races.

Galloway's Performance Predictor

Step 1: Run your "magic mile" time trial (MM) (4 laps around the track)

Step 2: (pace predicted is a very hard effort)

Half marathon predicted pace: multiply MM by 1.2

Marathon predicted pace: multiply MM by 1.3

10 Mile predicted pace: multiply MM by 1.175

Example: Magic Mile time: 10:00

Marathon pace: 10 x 1.3 = 13 minutes per mile

Half marathon pace: 10 x 1.2= 12 minutes per mile

10 Mile pace: 10 x 1.175 = 11:45 pace per mile

Long run training pace = 15 minutes per mile (add 2 minutes per mile to marathon pace regardless of goal distance)

In order to run the time in the race indicated by Galloway's Performance Predictor:

- You have done the training necessary for the goal—according to the training programs in this book.

- You are not injured.

- You run with an even-paced effort.

- The weather on goal race day is below 60°F or 14°C, with no strong headwinds, no heavy rain or snow, etc.

- There are no crowds to run through or significant hills.

HOW HARD SHOULD I RUN THE TEST

During the first month of the program, you could run the magic mile about every other week, in the middle of a Tuesday or Thursday run. The first one should be only slightly faster than you normally run. With each successive MM, pick up the pace and beat your previous best time. By the fourth

one, you should be running fairly close to your current potential.

Improvement Strategy: Run the first lap slightly slower than you think you can average. If you aren't huffing and puffing, you can pick up the pace a bit on second lap. If you are huffing after the first lap, then just hold your pace on lap two—or reduce it slightly. Many find that they record a faster time by walking for 10 to 30 seconds after one or two of the laps, but this is optional. It is okay to be breathing hard on the last lap. If you are slowing down on the last lap, start a little slower on the next test. When you finish, you should feel like you couldn't run more than about half a lap further at that pace (if that). You may find that you don't need many walk breaks during the MM—experiment and adjust.

FIRST TIME PARTICIPANTS—RUN TO FINISH ONLY

I strongly recommend that first participants, in any event, run at a comfortable training pace. Use the prediction formula above to determine long run pace (adding 2 minutes to the time multiplied by 1.3). During the race itself, I recommend running the first 75 percent of the race at your training pace. During the last 25 percent of the race, you may run as you wish.

TIME GOAL RUNNERS MAY MAKE A "LEAP OF FAITH" GOAL PREDICTION

I have no problem allowing my Ecoach athletes, who've run one or more races at a given distance, to choose a goal time that is faster than that predicted by the first 3-4 MMs. As you do the speed training, the long runs and your test races, you should improve...but how much? In my experience this "leap of faith" should not exceed 3 to 5 percent improvement in a 3-month training program.

1. Run the magic mile, 3 or 4 times.

2. Take your fastest time and use the formula above to predict current per mile goal pace now, if you were trained for your race.

3. Choose the amount of improvement during the training program (3-5%).

4. Subtract this from # 2—this is your goal time.

Note: This assumes that all of the training is done to achieve the goal.

The key to goal-setting is keeping your ego in check. From my experience, I have found that a 3 percent improvement is realistic. In

14

Galloway's Performance Predictor

Predicted goal pace after 3-4 MM's	3% Improvement	5% Improvement
6 min/mi	5:48/mile	5:42/mile
7 min/mi	6:48/mile	6:39/mile
8 min/mi	7:46/mile	7:36/mile
9 min/mi	8:44/mile	8:33/mile
10 min/mi	9:42/mile	9:30/mile
11 min/mi	10:40/mile	10:27/mile
12 min/mi	11:38/mile	11:24/mile
13 min/mi	12:37/mile	12:21/mile
14 min/mi	13:35/mile	13:18/mile
15 min/mi	14:33/mile	14:15/mile
16 min/mi	15:31/mile	15:12/mile
17 min/mi	16:29/mile	16:09/mile
18 min/mi	17:27/mile	17:06/mile
19 min/mi	18:25/mile	18:03/mile
20 min/mi	19:23/mile	19:00/mile

both of these situations, everything must come together to produce the predicted result. Even runners who shoot for a 3 percent improvement, do all the training as described, have a goal success rate of over 60 percent (after an average of 3 goal races, from surveys). The maximum 5 percent improvement is less likely but is achieved (after an average of 3 tries) in about 40 percent of the folks I've surveyed. There are many factors that determine a time goal in a race that are outside of your control: weather, terrain, infection, etc.

"MAGIC MILE" (MM) TIME TRIALS GIVE YOU A REALITY CHECK BEFORE YOUR GOAL RACE

♦ Try to run every one of the MMs on the schedule.

♦ Adjust pace on each lap so that you run a little faster during the last 2 laps.

♦ Hint: hold yourself back on the first lap.

♦ Most runners will improve the MM on most attempts if training is done and rest days are taken.

♦ If you are not making progress, look for reasons and take action.

♦ The fastest time run during the last few MMs will predict a very hard race pace.

♦ You can then adjust your pace due to temperature and effort level desired.

Reasons why you may not be improving:

1. You're over-trained and tired—if so, reduce your training and/or take an extra rest day.

2. You may have chosen a goal that is too ambitious for your current ability.

3. You may have missed some of your workouts or not been as regular with your training as needed.

4. The temperature may have been above 60° F (14° C). Above this, you will slow down. (The longer the race, the more effect heat will make on the result.)

5. You ran the first lap or two too fast.

Conservative pacing: It is strongly recommended that you run the first one-third of your goal race a few seconds a mile slower than the pace predicted by the best MM time.

USE A JOURNAL!

Read the chapter on using a journal. Your chance of reaching your goal increases greatly with this very important instrument. Psychologically, you start taking responsibility for the fulfillment of your mission when you use a journal.

15

GALLOWAY TRAINING SCHEDULES:

CONDITIONING, 10 MILE, HALF MARATHON, MARATHON

CONDITIONING PROGRAM

(for those who need a little more fitness before the program begins)

Mon	Tues	Wed	Thu	Fri	Sat	Sun
Week 1 *(walkers will walk only, runners will run for 5 seconds/walk for 55 seconds on the run/walk days)*						
10 min run/walk	15 min walk	13 min run/walk	18 min walk	off	1 mile run/walk	off/walk
Week 2 *(walkers will walk only, runners will run for 5 seconds/walk for 55 seconds on the run/walk days)*						
15 min run/walk	20 min walk	17 min run/walk	22 min walk	off	1.25 mi run/walk	off/walk
Week 3 *(walkers will walk only, runners will run for 10 seconds/walk for 50 seconds on the run/walk days)*						
19 min run/walk	24 min walk	21 min run/walk	26 min walk	off	1.5 mi run/walk	off/walk
Week 4 *(walkers will walk only, runners will run for10 seconds/walk for 50 seconds on the run/walk days)*						
23 min run/walk	28 min walk	25 min run/walk	30 min walk	off	1.75 mi run/walk	off/walk
Week 5 *(walkers will walk only, runners will run for 10 seconds/walk for 50 seconds on the run/walk days)*						
27 min run/walk	28 min walk	29 min run/walk	30 min walk	off	2 mi run/ walk	off/walk
Week 6 *(walkers will walk only, runners will run for 15 seconds/walk for 45 seconds on the run/walk days)*						
30 min run/walk	28 min walk	30 min run/walk	30 min walk	off	2.25 mi run/walk	off/walk
Week 7 *(walkers will walk only, runners will run for 15 seconds/walk for 45 seconds on the run/walk days)*						
30 min run/walk	28 min walk	30 min run/walk	30 min walk	off	2.5 mi run/walk	off/walk
Week 8 *(walkers will walk only, runners will run for 15 seconds/walk for 45 seconds on the run/walk days)*						
30 min run/walk	28 min walk	30 min run/walk	30 min walk	off	2.75 mi run/walk	off/walk

Note: if you need several weeks at each run/walk ratio level, take it. This pre-conditioning training should not be stressful or painful. When in doubt, ease off.

10 MILE

To Finish – for runners and walkers

This program is designed for those who have been doing some running or walking for a few weeks. If you think that you need more conditioning before starting the program, use the "conditioning program" above.

Note: This is the minimum that I've found necessary to finish with strength. If you are already running/walking more than this amount and are able to recover between workouts, you may continue to do what you are doing—but be careful.

Note for walkers: Walk the distances noted on the schedule. On the "easy walk" days, take more shuffle walks and walk slower.

1. I don't recommend that first-time 10-mile participants try for a time goal. Do the first one to finish, running/walking at a comfortable training pace.

2. To begin this program, you should have done a long run/walk within the past 2 weeks of at least 3 miles. If your long one is not this long, then gradually increase the weekend run/walk to this distance before starting this program.

3. (Runners) What is my current level of performance? Read the chapter in the book on "Choosing The Right Goal...". After you have run 3-4 "magic miles" (MM), multiply by 1.175. This tells you what you are currently capable of running 10 miles right now (at a very hard pace), when the temperature is 60° F or below, and that you have done the long runs and speed training listed in the schedule. Even in the 10-mile race itself, I don't recommend running this fast—run at the training pace that was comfortable for you on your last long runs.

4. (Runners) What pace should I run on the long ones? Take your magic mile time and multiply by 1.3. Then add 2 minutes. The result is your suggested long run pace per mile on long runs at 60° F or cooler. It is always better to run slower than this pace.

5. Walkers and runners should pace the long one so there's no huffing and puffing—even at the end.

6. When the temperature rises above 60° F: runners slow down by 30 seconds a mile for every 5 degrees above 60° F. Walkers, slow down enough to avoid huffing and puffing.

7. Run-walk-run ratio should correspond to the pace used (Runners).

   8 min/mi—run 4 min/walk 30 seconds

   9 min/mi—4 min run-1 min walk

   10 min/mi—3-1

   11 min/mi—2:30-1

   12 min/mi—2-1

   13 min/mi—1-1

   14 min/mi—30 sec run/30 sec walk

   15 min/mi—30 sec/45 sec

   16 min/mi—30 sec/60 sec

   Walkers—use the walk-shuffle ratio that works for you to avoid huffing and puffing.

8. It is fine to do cross training on Monday, Wednesday and Friday if you wish. There will be little benefit to your running/walking in doing this, but you'll increase your fat-burning potential. Don't do exercises like stair machines that use the calf muscle on cross training days.

9. Be sure to take a vacation from strenuous exercise on the day before your weekend runs/walks.

10. Have fun!

Mon	Tues	Wed	Thur (p)	Fri	Sat	Sun
1. off	30 min run	off	30 min run	easy walk	off	3 miles
2. off	30 min run	off	30 min run	easy walk	off	4 mi MM
3. off	30 min run	off	30 min run	easy walk	off	5 miles
4. off	30 min run	off	30 min run	easy walk	off	2.5 mi MM
5. off	30 min run	off	30 min run	easy walk	off	6.5 miles
6. off	30 min run	off	30 min run	easy walk	off	3 mi MM
7. off	30 min run	off	30 min run	easy walk	off	8 miles
8. off	30 min run	off	30 min run	easy walk	off	3 mi MM
9. off	30 min run	off	30 min run	easy walk	off	9.5 miles
10. off	30 min run	off	30 min run	easy walk	off	4 miles MM
11. off	30 min run	off	30 min run	easy walk	off	11 miles
12. off	30 min run	off	30 min run	easy walk	off	4 mi MM
13. off	30 min run	off	30 min run	easy walk	off	10 mi Goal
14. off	30 min run	off	30 min run	easy walk	off	4 mi
15. off	30 min run	off	30 min run	easy walk	off	5-8 miles

19

10 MILE

Time Goal Program For Runners

Note: This is the minimum that I've found necessary to prepare for the goal. If you are already running more than this amount and are able to recover between workouts, you may continue to do what you are doing—but be careful.

1. I don't recommend that first-time 10-mile participants try for a time goal. Run the first one to finish, running mostly at a comfortable training pace.

2. To begin this program, you should have done a long run within the past 2 weeks of at least 5 miles. If your long one is not this long, gradually increase the weekend run to this distance before starting this program.

3. What is my current level of performance? Read the chapter in the book on "Choosing The Right Goal...". After you have run 3-4 "magic miles" (MM), multiply by 1.175. This tells you what you are currently capable of running in a 10-miler (at a very hard effort), right now, when the temperature is 60° F or below, and when you have done the long runs and speed training listed in the schedule.

4. What pace should I run on the long ones? Take your MM time and multiply by 1.3. Then add 2 minutes. The result is your suggested long run pace per mile on long runs at 60° F or cooler. It is always better to run slower than this pace.

5. Pace the long one so that you aren't huffing and puffing—even at the end.

6. When the temperature rises above 60° F: Slow down by 30 seconds a mile for every 5 degrees above 60° F.

7. Run-walk-run ratio should correspond to the pace used.

   8 min/mi—run 4 min/walk 30 seconds

   9 min/mi—4 min run-1 min walk

   10 min/mi—3-1

   11 min/mi—2:30-1

   12 min/mi—2-1

   13 min/mi—1-1

   14 min/mi—30 sec run/30 sec walk

   15 min/mi—30 sec/45 sec

   16 min/mi—30 sec/60 sec

8. It is fine to do cross training on Monday, Wednesday and Friday if you wish. There will be little benefit to your running in doing this, but you'll increase your fat-burning potential. Don't do exercises like stair machines that use the calf muscle on non-running days.

9. Be sure to take a vacation from strenuous exercise on the day before your weekend runs.

10. At the beginning of the program, after you have run 2 MMs, you can choose a goal that is as fast as 30 seconds per mile faster than predicted by the process indicated in # 3—or any goal that is slower than this. *(Read the "leap of faith goal" segment of the "Choosing The Right Pace" chapter.)*

11. To prepare for your goal, 800-meter speedwork is included on non-long-run weekends. To compute your pace for the 800-meter (2 laps around a track), take half the time of your goal pace per mile, as you decided according to #10 above, and subtract 15 seconds.

12. Warm up for each 800-meter repeat workout by walking for 5 minutes, then jogging very slowly for 5-10 minutes. Then do 4-8 acceleration-gliders. (See the segment about this in "Drills" chapter of this book.) Reverse this process as your warm down, leaving out the acceleration gliders.

13. Walk 2:30 to 3 minutes between each 800-meter repeat.

Mon	Tues	Wed	Thur	Fri	Sat	Sun
1. off	30 min run	off	30 min run	easy walk	off	5 miles
2. off	35 min run MM	off	35 min run	easy walk	off	6 mi
3. off	35 min run	off	35 min run	easy walk	off	7 mi
4. off	40 min run MM	off	40 min run	easy walk	off	4 x 800
5. off	40 min run	off	40 min run	easy walk	off	8.5 mi
6. off	45 min run MM	off	45 min run	easy walk	off	7 x 800
7. off	45 min run	off	45 min run	easy walk	off	10 miles
8. off	45 min run MM	off	45 min run	easy walk	off	9 x 800
9. off	45 min run	off	45 min run	easy walk	off	12 miles
10. off	45 min run	off	45 min run	easy walk	off	10-12 x 800
11. off	45 min run	off	45 min run	easy walk	off	14 miles
12. off	45 min run	off	45 min run	easy walk	off	4 mi MM
13. off	45 min run	off	45 min run	easy walk	off	10 mi Goal
14. off	45 min run	off	45 min run	easy walk	off	6 miles
15. off	45 min run	off	45 min run	easy walk	off	7 miles

21

14. At the end of the first lap, walk for 10-30 seconds—but don't stop your stopwatch. The time for each 800 should be from the start until you finish the second lap.

15. If you have recovered from the weekend workout by Tuesday, run a mile at race pace (noted as "p" on the Tuesday line). After an easy warmup, run 4 of the cadence drills (CD) and 4 acceleration-gliders (Acg). These are described in the Drill section of my book. Then run a mile segment at goal pace, taking the walk breaks as you plan to do them in the race. Jog for the rest of your run.

16. On long runs and the race itself, slow down when the temperature rises above 60° F: by 30 seconds a mile for every 5 degrees above 60° F or more.

17. Have fun!

HALF MARATHON

To Finish—for runners and walkers

This program is designed for those who have been doing some running or walking for a few weeks. If you think that you need more conditioning before starting the program, use the "conditioning program" above.

Note: This is the minimum that I've found necessary to finish with strength. If you are already running/walking more than this amount and are able to recover between workouts, you may continue to do what you are doing—but be careful.

Note for walkers: Walk the distances noted on the schedule. On the "easy walk" days, take more shuffle walks and walk slower.

1. I don't recommend that first-time half marathon participants try for a time goal. Do the first one to finish, running/walking at a comfortable training pace.

2. To begin this program, you should have done a long run/walk within the past 2 weeks of at least 3 miles. If your long one is not this long, then gradually increase the weekend run/walk to this distance before starting this program.

3. (Runners) What is my current level of performance? Read the chapter in the book on "Choosing The Right Goal...". After you have run 3-4 "magic miles" (MM), multiply by 1.2. This tells you what you are currently capable of running in a half marathon right now (at a very hard effort), when the temperature is 60° F or below and when you have done the long runs listed in the schedule. Even in the half marathon itself, I don't recommend running this fast—run at the training pace that was comfortable for you on your last long runs.

4. (Runners) What pace should I run on the long ones? Take your MM time and multiply by 1.3. Then add 2 minutes. The result is your suggested long run pace per mile on long runs at 60F or cooler. It is always better to run slower than this pace.

5. Walkers and runners should pace the long one so there's no huffing and puffing—even at the end.

6. When the temperature rises above 60° F: runners slow down by 30 seconds a mile for every 5 degrees above 60° F. Walkers slow down enough to avoid huffing and puffing.

7. Run-walk-run ratio should correspond to the pace used (Runners).

   8 min/mi—run 4 min/walk 30 seconds

   9 min/mi—4 min run-1 min walk

   10 min/mi—3-1

   11 min/mi—2:30-1

   12 min/mi—2-1

   13 min/mi—1-1

   14 min/mi—30 sec run/30 sec walk

   15 min/mi—30 sec/45 sec

   16 min/mi—30 sec/60 sec

8. Walkers—use the walk-shuffle ratio that works for you to avoid huffing and puffing

9. It is fine to do cross training on Monday, Wednesday and Friday if you wish. There will be little benefit to your running/walking in doing this, but you'll increase your fat-burning potential. Don't do exercises like stair machines that use the calf muscle on cross training days.

10. Be sure to take a vacation from strenuous exercise on the day before your weekend runs/walks.

11. Have fun!

Mon	Tues	Wed	Thur (p)	Fri	Sat	Sun
1. off	20 min run	off	25 min run	easy walk	off	3 miles
2. off	30 min run	off	30 min run	easy walk	off	4 miles
3. off	30 min run	off	30 min run	easy walk	off	5 miles
4. off	30 min run	off	30 min run	easy walk	off	2.5 mi MM
5. off	30 min run	off	30 min run	easy walk	off	6.5 miles
6. off	30 min run	off	30 min run	easy walk	off	3 mi MM
7. off	30 min run	off	30 min run	easy walk	off	8 miles
8. off	30 min run	off	30 min run	easy walk	off	3 mi MM
9. off	30 min run	off	30 min run	easy walk	off	9.5 miles
10. off	30 min run	off	30 min run	easy walk	off	4 miles
11. off	30 min run	off	30 min run	easy walk	off	11 miles
12. off	30 min run	off	30 min run	easy walk	off	4 mi MM
13. off	30 min run	off	30 min run	easy walk	off	12.5 miles
14. off	30 min run	off	30 min run	easy walk	off	4 mi MM
15. off	30 min run	off	30 min run	easy walk	off	14 miles
16. off	30 min run	off	30 min run	easy walk	off	5 miles
17. off	30 min run	off	30 min run	easy walk	off	Half Goal Race
18. off	30 min run	off	30 min run	easy walk	off	5 miles
19. off	30 min run	off	30 min run	easy walk	off	6-8 miles

23

Galloway Training   **www.JeffGalloway.com**

HALF MARATHON

Time Goal for runners

Note: This is the minimum that I've found necessary to prepare for the goal. If you are already running more than this amount and are able to recover between workouts, you may continue to do what you are doing—but be careful.

1. I don't recommend that first-time half marathoners try for a time goal. Run the first one to finish, running mostly at a comfortable training pace.

2. To begin this program, you should have done a long run within the past 2 weeks of at least 5 miles. If your long one is not this long, gradually increase the weekend run to this distance before starting this program.

3. What is my current level of performance? Read the chapter in the book on "Choosing The Right Goal...". After you have run 3-4 "magic miles" (MM), multiply by 1.2. This tells you what you are currently capable of running in a half marathon right now (at a very hard effort), when the temperature is 60° F or below and when you have done the long runs and speed training listed in the schedule.

4. What pace should I run on the long ones? Take your MM time and multiply by 1.3. Then add 2 minutes. The result is your suggested long run pace per mile on long runs at 60° F or cooler. It is always better to run slower than this pace.

5. Pace the long one so that you aren't huffing and puffing—even at the end.

6. When the temperature rises above 60° F: Slow down by 30 seconds a mile for every 5 degrees above 60° F on long runs and the race itself.

7. Run-walk-run ratio should correspond to the pace used.

   8 min/mi—run 4 min/walk 30 seconds

   9 min/mi—4 min run-1 min walk

10 min/mi—3-1

11 min/mi—2:30-1

12 min/mi—2-1

13 min/mi—1-1

14 min/mi—30 sec run/30 sec walk

15 min/mi—30 sec/45 sec

16 min/mi—30 sec/60 sec

8. It is fine to do cross training on Monday, Wednesday and Friday if you wish. There will be little benefit to your running in doing this, but you'll increase your fat-burning potential. Don't do exercises like stair machines that use the calf muscle on non-running days.

9. Be sure to take a vacation from strenuous exercise on the day before your weekend runs.

10. At the beginning of the program, after you have run 2 MMs, you can choose a goal that is as fast as 30 seconds per mile faster than predicted by the process indicated in # 3—or any goal that is slower than this. *(Read the "leap of faith goal" segment of the "Choosing The Right Pace" chapter.)*

11. To prepare for your goal, 800-meter speedwork is included on non-long-run weekends. To compute your pace for the 800-meter (2 laps around a track), take half the time of your goal pace per mile, as you decided according to #10 above, and subtract 15 seconds.

12. Warm up for each 800-meter repeat workout by walking for 5 minutes, then jogging very slowly for 5-10 minutes. Then do 4-8 acceleration-gliders *(see the segment about this in "Drills" chapter of this book)*. Reverse this process as your warm down, leaving out the acceleration gliders.

13. Walk 2:30 to 3 min between each 800-meter repeat.

Mon	Tues (p)	Wed	Thur	Fri	Sat	Sun
1. off	30 min run	off	30 min run	easy walk	off	5 miles
2. off	35 min run MM	off	35 min run	easy walk	off	6 mi
3. off	35 min run	off	35 min run	easy walk	off	7.5 mi
4. off	40 min run MM	off	40 min run	easy walk	off	4 x 800
5. off	40 min run	off	40 min run	easy walk	off	9 mi
6. off	45 min run MM	off	45 min run	easy walk	off	6 x 800
7. off	45 min run	off	45 min run	easy walk	off	11 miles
8. off	45 min run MM	off	45 min run	easy walk	off	8 x 800
9. off	45 min run	off	45 min run	easy walk	off	13 miles
10. off	45 min run	off	45 min run	easy walk	off	10 x 800
11. off	45 min run	off	45 min run	easy walk	off	15 miles
12. off	45 min run	off	45 min run	easy walk	off	12 x 800
13. off	45 min run	off	45 min run	easy walk	off	17 miles
14. off	45 min run	off	45 min run	easy walk	off	Easy 5 miles MM
15. off	45 min run	off	45 min run	easy walk	off	Goal Half Race
16. off	45 min run	off	45 min run	easy walk	off	4 miles
17. off	45 min run	off	45 min run	easy walk	off	6-12 miles

25

14. At the end of the first lap, walk for 10-30 seconds—but don't stop your stopwatch. The time for each 800 should be from the start until you finish the second lap.

15. If you have recovered from the weekend workout on Tuesday, run a mile at race pace (noted as "p" on the Tue line). After an easy warmup, run 4 of the cadence drills (CD) and 4 acceleration-gliders (Acg). These are described in the Drill section of my book. Then run a mile segment at goal pace, taking the walk breaks as you plan to do them in the race. Jog for the rest of your run.

16. On long runs and the race itself, slow down when the temperature rises above 60° F: by 30 seconds a mile for every 5 degrees above 60° F or more.

17. Have fun!

MARATHON
To Finish—for runners and walkers

This program is designed for those who have been doing some running or walking for a few weeks. If you think that you need more conditioning before starting the program, use the "conditioning program" above.

Note: This is the minimum that I've found necessary to finish with strength. If you are already running/walking more than this amount and are able to recover between workouts, you may continue to do what you are doing—but be careful.

Note for walkers: Walk the distances noted on the schedule. On the "easy walk" days, take more shuffle walks and walk slower.

1. I don't recommend that first-time marathon participants try for a time goal. Do the first one to finish, running/walking at a comfortable training pace.

2. To begin this program, you should have done a long run/walk within the past 2 weeks of at least 3 miles. If your long one is not this long, gradually increase the weekend run/walk to this distance before starting this program.

3. (Runners) What is my current level of performance? Read the chapter in this book on "Choosing The Right Goal...". After you have run 3-4 "magic miles" (MM), multiply by 1.3. This tells you what you are currently capable of running in a marathon right now (at a very hard effort), when the temperature is 60° F or below and when you have done the long runs listed in the schedule. Even in the marathon itself, I don't recommend running this fast—run at the training pace that was comfortable for you on your last long runs.

4. (Runners) What pace should I run on the long ones? Take your MM time and multiply by 1.3. Then add 2 minutes. The result is your suggested long run pace per mile on long runs at 60° F or cooler. It is always better to run slower than this pace.

5. Walkers and runners should pace the long one so there's no huffing and puffing—even at the end.

6. When the temperature rises above 60° F: runners should slow down by 30 seconds a mile for every 5 degrees above 60° F on long runs and the race itself. Walkers, slow down enough to avoid huffing and puffing.

7. Run-walk-run ratio should correspond to the pace used (Runners).

   8 min/mi—run 4 min/walk 30 seconds

   9 min/mi—4 min run-1 min walk

   10 min/mi—3-1

   11 min/mi—2:30-1

   12 min/mi—2-1

   13 min/mi—1-1

   14 min/mi—30 sec run/30 sec walk

   15 min/mi—30 sec/45 sec

   16 min/mi—30 sec/60 sec

8. Walkers—use the walk-shuffle ratio that works for you to avoid huffing and puffing

9. It is fine to do cross training on Monday, Wednesday and Friday if you wish. There will be little benefit to your running/walking in doing this, but you'll increase your fat-burning potential. Don't do exercises like stair machines that use the calf muscle on cross training days.

10. Be sure to take a vacation from strenuous exercise on the day before your weekend runs/walks.

11. Have fun!

Mon	Tues	Wed	Thur (p)	Fri	Sat	Sun
1. off	30 min run	off	30 min run	easy walk	off	3 miles
2. off	30 min run	off	30 min run	easy walk	off	4 mi
3. off	30 min run	off	30 min run	easy walk	off	5 miles
4. off	30 min run	off	30 min run	easy walk	off	2.5 mi MM
5. off	30 min run	off	30 min run	easy walk	off	6 miles
6. off	30 min run	off	30 min run	easy walk	off	3 mi
7. off	30 min run	off	30 min run	easy walk	off	7.5 miles
8. off	30 min run	off	30 min run	easy walk	off	3 mi MM
9. off	30 min run	off	30 min run	easy walk	off	9 miles
10. off	30 min run	off	30 min run	easy walk	off	4 miles
11. off	30 min run	off	30 min run	easy walk	off	10.5 miles
12. off	30 min run	off	30 min run	easy walk	off	4 mi MM
13. off	30 min run	off	30 min run	easy walk	off	12 miles
14. off	30 min run	off	30 min run	easy walk	off	4 miles
15. off	30 min run	off	30 min run	easy walk	off	14 miles
16. off	30 min run	off	30 min run	easy walk	off	5 mi MM
17. off	30 min run	off	30 min run	easy walk	off	17 miles
18. off	30 min run	off	30 min run	easy walk	off	5 miles
19. off	30 min run	off	30 min run	easy walk	off	6 mi MM
20. off	30 min run	off	30 min run	easy walk	off	20 miles
21. off	30 min run	off	30 min run	easy walk	off	6 miles
22. off	30 min run	off	30 min run	easy walk	off	6 mi MM
23. off	30 min run	off	30 min run	easy walk	off	23 miles
24. off	30 min run	off	30 min run	easy walk	off	6 miles
25. off	30 min run	off	30 min run	easy walk	off	7 miles
26. off	30 min run	off	30 min run	easy walk	off	26 miles
27. off	30 min run	off	30 min run	easy walk	off	7 miles
28. off	30 min run	off	30 min run	easy walk	off	6 miles
29. off	30 min run	off	30 min run	easy walk	off	7 miles
30. off	30 min run	off	30 min run	easy walk	off	Marathon
31. off	30 min run	off	30 min run	easy walk	off	4 miles
32. off	30 min run	off	30 min run	easy walk	off	6 miles

27

MARATHON

Time Goal—for runners

Note: This is the minimum that I've found necessary to prepare for the goal. If you are already running more than this amount and are able to recover between workouts, you may continue to do what you are doing—but be careful.

1. I don't recommend that first-time marathoners try for a time goal. Run the first one to finish, running mostly at a comfortable training pace.

2. To begin this program, you should have done a long run within the past 2 weeks of at least 7 miles. If your long one is not this long, gradually increase the weekend run to this distance before starting this program.

3. What is my current level of performance? Read the chapter in the book on "Choosing The Right Goal...". After you have run 3-4 "magic miles" (MM), multiply by 1.3. This tells you what you are currently capable of running in a marathon right now (at a very hard effort), when the temperature is 60° F or below and when you have done the long runs and speed training listed in the schedule.

4. What pace should I run on the long ones? Take your MM time and multiply by 1.3. Then add 2 minutes. The result is your suggested long run pace per mile on long runs at 60° F or cooler. It is always better to run slower than this pace.

5. Pace the long one so that you aren't huffing and puffing—even at the end.

6. When the temperature rises above 60° F: Slow down by 30 seconds a mile on long runs and the race itself for every 5 degrees above 60° F.

7. Run-walk-run ratio should correspond to the pace used.

    8 min/mi—run 4 min/walk 30 seconds

    9 min/mi—4 min run-1 min walk

10 min/mi—3-1

11 min/mi—2:30-1

12 min/mi—2-1

13 min/mi—1-1

14 min/mi—30 sec run/30 sec walk

15 min/mi—30 sec/45 sec

16 min/mi—30 sec/60 sec

8. At the beginning of the program, after you have run 2 MMs, you can choose a goal that is as fast as 30 seconds per mile faster than predicted by the process indicated in # 3—or any goal that is slower than this. *(Read the "leap of faith goal" segment of the "Choosing The Right Pace" chapter.)*

9. To prepare for your goal, 1-mile repetition speedwork is included on non-long-run weekends. To compute your pace for the mile (4 laps around a track), use the goal pace decided according to #8 above and subtract 30 seconds. Example: a runner who has set the "leap of faith" goal at 10 min/mile in the marathon would be running mile repeats in 9:30 each.

10. Warm up for each mile repeat workout by walking for 5 minutes and then jog very slowly for 5-10 minutes. Then do 4-8 acceleration-gliders. *(See the segment about this in "Drills" chapter of this book.)* Reverse this process as your warm down, leaving out the acceleration gliders.

11. Walk 5 minutes between each 1-mile repeat.

12. During the 1-mile repeats, run the amount you will be running in the race itself and walk for 30 seconds—but don't stop your stopwatch. The time for each mile repeat should be from the start until you finish the second lap. For example, a person with a time goal of 10 min/mile in the marathon would run 9:30 for each mile repeat. This

Mon	Tue (CD/acg/p)	Wed	Thursday (h)	Fri	Sat	Sun
1. off	30 min run	off	30 min run	easy walk	off	7.5 miles
2. off	30 min run	off	0 min run	easy walk	off	9 miles
3. off	35 min run	off	35 min run	easy walk	off	5 mi MM
4. off	35 min run	off	35 min run	easy walk	off	11 miles
5. off	40 min run	off	40 min run	easy walk	off	5 miles
6. off	40 min run	off	40 min run	easy walk	off	13 miles
7. off	40 min run	off	40 min run	easy walk	off	5 mi MM
8. off	40 min run	off	40 min run	easy walk	off	15 miles
9. off	40 min run	off	40 min run	easy walk	off	4 x 1 mi
10. off	40 min run	off	40 min run	easy walk	off	17mi
11. off	40 min run	off	40 min run	easy walk	off	6 x 1mi
12. off	40 min run	off	40 min run	easy walk	off	6 mi MM
13. off	40 min run	off	40 min run	easy walk	off	20 miles
14. off	45 min run	off	45 min run	easy walk	off	8 x 1 mi
15. off	45 min run	off	45 min run	easy walk	off	7 mi MM
16. off	45 min run	off	45 min run	easy walk	off	23 mi
17. off	45 min run	off	45 min run	easy walk	off	10x 1 mi
18. off	45 min run	off	45 min run	easy walk	off	6 mi MM
19. off	45 min run	off	45 min run	easy walk	off	26 mi
20. off	45 min run	off	45 min run	easy walk	off	6 miles
21. off	45 min run	off	45 min run	easy walk	off	12 x 1mi
22. off	45 min run	off	45 min run	easy walk	off	6mi MM
23. off	45 min run	off	45 min run	easy walk	off	29 miles
24. off	45 min run	off	45 min run	easy walk	off	6 miles
25. off	45 min run	off	45 min run	easy walk	off	14x1 mi
26. off	45 min run	off	45 min run	easy walk	off	7 miles
27. off	30 min run	off	30 min run	easy walk	off	Marathon
28. off	30 min run	off	30 min run	easy walk	off	4 miles
29. off	30 min run	off	30 min run	easy walk	off	6 miles

29

Galloway Training   **www.JeffGalloway.com**

person should run for 3 minutes and walk for 30 seconds while the watch is running during each mile repeat.

13. If you have recovered from the weekend workout on Tuesday, run 1-3 miles at race pace (noted as "p" on the Tue line). After an easy warmup, run 4 of the cadence drills (CD) and 4 acceleration-gliders (Acg). These are described in the Drill section of my book. Then run a segment at goal pace (your choice, 1-3 miles), taking the walk breaks as you plan to do them in the race. Jog for the rest of your run. Example: A runner training for a 10-minute pace in the marathon would shoot for 10-minute pace during each mile of the "marathon pace" segment, running for 3 minutes and walking for one minute—with the watch running.

14. If your marathon goal race has some hills on the course, you can run some hills on Thursday if you've recovered from your weekend run. Insert 1-4 hill accelerations ("h" on the schedule). Warm up and warm down with an easy 1-2 miles. Run up the hill at a fast but not all-out pace and walk down. Use a short stride with quick turnover as you go up the hill.

Have Fun!

WALK AND SHUFFLE BREAKS

THE GALLOWAY
RUN-WALK-RUN METHOD

"Without breaks, I could only go three miles, with difficulty. Using breaks, I've finished three marathons feeling strong."

WALK/SHUFFLE BREAKS WILL...

...allow those who can only go two miles to go three or four and feel fine

...help beginners, older or heavy runners/walkers to increase their endurance to 5K, 10K or even the half or full marathon in as soon as six months

...bestow the endurance for runners/walkers of all abilities to go beyond "the wall"

... allow runners/walkers over the age of 40 to not only do their first half or full marathon but to improve times in most cases

...help runners/walkers of all ages to improve times because legs are strong at the end

...reduce the chance of injury and over-training to almost nothing

As one who has pridefully run for more than four decades, it's sometimes hard to admit something, but here goes. Our bodies weren't designed to run continuously for long distances, especially distances as far as the marathon. Sure we can adapt, but there is a better way to increase endurance than by running continuously. By alternating walking and running, from the start, there's virtually no limit to the distance you can cover. Thousands of people in their 40s and 50s with no exercise background have used my run-walk-run method to complete a marathon in six months. Once we find the ideal ratio for a given distance, walk/shuffle breaks allow us to feel strong to the end and recover fast, while bestowing the same stamina and conditioning we would have received if we had run continuously.

Most runners will record significantly faster times when they take walk breaks because they don't slow down at the end of a long run. Thousands of time-goal-oriented vet-erans have improved by 10, 20, 30 minutes and more in half or full marathons by taking walk breaks early and often in their goal race. You can easily spot these folks in races. They're the ones who are picking up speed during the last two to six miles when everyone else is slowing down.

WALK-RUNNING IS WHAT WE WERE DESIGNED TO DO

Our ancient ancestors had to walk and run thousands of miles every year to survive. Because they moved on to greener pastures and away from predators, we're here to philosophize about walk breaks. So it's a fact that each of us inherited an organism that was designed to move forward for long distances. As often happens with behaviors which enhance survival, a series of very complex and internally satisfying rewards have developed, which relax the muscles, stimulate the creative and intuitive side of our brain and energize our spirit. By

> **"W**hen I moved my weekend long one up to 10 miles, I started to feel, after each long one, some primitive feelings—like I was the first one blazing a trail for others to follow."

getting out the door and moving forward three or more times a week, even the most out-of-shape couch potato will discover this enhanced sense of self worth and improved attitude.

While walking is our most efficient exercise pattern, we can adapt to running/walking and do well. Indeed, most walkers who add running to their exercise say they get a better boost in their after-exercise attitude. But running continuously can quickly push anyone beyond the capacity of leg muscles. When we alternate between walking and running, early and often, we are going back to the type of exertion that brought our forebears across continents, through deserts and over mountain ranges.

EVEN A SHORT WALK/SHUFFLE BREAK WHEN TAKEN EARLY AND REGULARLY WILL:

- Extend the capacity of the running/walking muscles at the end of the workout because you're shifting the workload between the walking and the running muscles

- Virtually erase fatigue with each early break by keeping your pace and effort level conservative in the early stages

- Allow those with some types of previous injuries to knees, ankles, hips, feet, etc. to train for half or full marathons without further injury

- Restore resiliency to the main running muscles before they fatigue—like getting a muscle strength booster shot each break

- Allow exercisers to improve 10 to 40 minutes in their full marathon compared with running continuously (3 to15 minutes in a half marathon)

- Speed up recovery from each long one even the very longest

- Leave you feeling good enough to carry on social and family activities—even after the very long long ones

WALK BREAKS WERE PART OF THE MARATHON——FROM THE BEGINNING

Ancient Greek messengers such as the original marathoner Phidippides [see his story in the first section of this book) regularly covered distances of more than 100 kilometers a day by walking and running. The accounts of the original marathon race, in the 1896 Olympics, described significant periods of walking for *all* competitors, including the winner Spiros Louis.

Elite marathoners continue to use walk breaks. The great American marathoner, Bill Rodgers, has said many times that he had to walk at water stations during his Boston and NYC marathon victories in order to get the water into his stomach (instead of wearing it on his shirt). Fabian Roncero took several walk breaks during his victory in the '98 Rotterdam Marathon to gather his resources. If anyone tells you that by taking walk breaks you are not a marathoner, he or she should be the one to tell this 2:07:26 champion that he is not a marathoner.

The label of "marathoner" has, from the beginning, been awarded to those who went the distance under their own power, whether they ran, walked, crawled or tiptoed. When you cross that finish line, you've entered an elite group. About two tenths of one percent of the population has done it. Don't let anyone take that great achievement away from you.

> **"I tried to train for three marathons without walk breaks and became injured each time. Walk breaks allowed me to get to the starting line and then to the marathon finish line...injury free!"**

I've now done over 130 marathons, about half of them without walk breaks. On every one of the walk-break marathons, I received the same sense of accomplishment, of the internal rewards and the indescribable exhilaration of finishing as on the non-walk marathons. But when I inserted walk breaks throughout, I was able to enjoy the accomplishment afterward.

WHY DO WALK/SHUFFLE BREAKS WORK?

BY USING MUSCLES IN DIFFERENT WAYS—FROM THE BEGINNING—YOUR LEGS KEEP THEIR BOUNCE AS THEY CONSERVE RESOURCES.

Walk/shuffle breaks keep you from using up your resources early. By alternating the exertion level and the way you're using your running/walking muscles, these prime movers have a chance to recover before they accumulate fatigue. On each successive walk, most or all of the fatigue is erased, bestowing strength at the end. This reduces the damage to the muscle dramatically, allowing you to carry on your life activities even after a long distance event.

Walk/shuffle breaks force you to slow down early in the session so that you don't start too fast. This reduction of the intensity of muscle use from the beginning conserves your energy, fluids and muscle capacity. On each walk/shuffle break, the running/walking muscles make internal adaptations, which give you the option to finish under control, increase the pace or go even further.

When a muscle group, such as your calf, is used continuously step by step, it fatigues relatively soon. The weak areas get over-used and force you to slow down later or scream at you in pain afterward. By

shifting back and forth between walking and running muscles (walking and shuffling muscles), you distribute the workload among a variety of muscles, increasing your overall performance capacity. For veteran marathoners, this is often the difference between achieving a time goal... or not.

Walk/shuffle breaks will significantly speed up recovery because there is less damage to repair. The early breaks erase fatigue, and the later breaks will reduce or eliminate overuse muscle breakdown.

WALK/SHUFFLE BREAKS CAN ELIMINATE INJURY

Many exercisers who were injured during previous training programs (because they ran continuously) have stayed injury-free when they add breaks to long ones. Without taking breaks from the beginning, the leg muscles fatigue more quickly and can't keep these lower extremities moving efficiently in their proper range of motion. The resulting "wobble" allows the leg to extend too far forward in an overstride. This abuses the tendons and injures the small muscle groups which try to keep the body on its proper mechanical track but don't have the horsepower to completely control the body weight moving forward.

Walk/shuffle breaks taken early in the workout keep the muscles strong and resilient enough so that the legs can move with strength and efficiency throughout. This will significantly reduce or eliminate the excess stress around the knees, ankles, feet, etc., which produces injury. The little "back-up" muscle groups can stay in reserve and fine-tune the run/walk motion after fatigue sets in.

HOW WALK BREAKS
AND SHUFFLE BREAKS
CAN SPEED YOU UP

A survey of veteran marathoners showed an average improvement of 13 minutes when they put walk breaks into their marathon, compared with running continuously under the same conditions. By saving the strength and efficiency of the running muscles through early walk breaks, you'll avoid the slowdown in the last six miles, where most continuous runners lose their momentum. You'll be passing people and picking up speed if you paced yourself conservatively and walked enough from the first mile.

WHY DO YOU SPEED UP WITH WALK BREAKS OR SHUFFLE BREAKS?

When you pace yourself correctly and take the walk/shuffle breaks you need in the first mile of a race, you'll virtually erase the fatigue of mile one. By continuing to walk/shuffle before you get tired, you conserve resources and can go with strength to the finish line. Most runners who don't take walk breaks slow down significantly during the last six to eight miles. Walk/shuffle-break-takers at least avoid the 7 to 15-minute slowdown at the end.

A GAME OF "CHASE"

After a few miles into your event, you'll settle into a pace and notice some of the folks around you. As you take your break, track one or two of them so that you catch up with them by the time you start your next break.

THE MENTAL BENEFIT: BREAKING DISTANCE INTO SEGMENTS WHICH YOU KNOW YOU CAN DO

Even sub-three-hour runners continue to take their walk breaks to the end. One of them explained it this way: "Instead of thinking at 20 miles that I had six more gut-wrenching miles to go, I was saying to myself 'one more mile until my break.' Even when it was tough, I always felt that I could go one more mile." A three-minute run/one minute walk person told me that she got over the tough parts by saying "three more minutes."

Walk and Shuffle Breaks: How Long and How Often?

The following is recommended until 18 miles (9 for half) in the marathon. After that point, breaks can be reduced or eliminated as desired.

Beginners should follow the program you've used in training as long as you aren't slowing down at the end of the long ones. If you struggled during the last few miles, take breaks more often from the beginning.

Run-Walk-Run Ratios for Runners

Here are my recommended ratios of running and walking, based upon your pace per mile. These ratios are in effect for both training runs and during the marathon itself.

Runners: Remember that long ones should be at least 2 min/mi slower than your projected finish pace in the half or full marathon. An additional slowdown should be made for increased temperature: 30 sec per mile slower for each 5 degrees of temperature increase above 60° F. It is always safer to take more frequent breaks.

Walkers: Shuffle for 30 seconds after 2 to 4 minutes of regular walking – from the beginning.

Recommended Ratios for Running: Walking

7 min/mi	1 mile	30 seconds
8 min/mi	4 min	30 seconds
9 min/mi	4 min	1 minute
10 min/mi	3 min	1 minute
11 min/mi	2:30	1 minute
12 min/mi	2 min	1 minute
13 min/mi	1 min	1 minute
14 min/mi	30 sec	30 sec
15 min/mi	30 sec	45 sec
16 min/mi	30 sec	60 sec
17 min/mi	20 sec	60 sec
18 min/mi	15 sec	60 sec
19 min/mi	10 sec	60 sec
20 min/mi	5-10 sec	60 sec

Jeff Galloway's Experience

His Choice: A 3:40 marathon *without* walking breaks...

or a 3:25 marathon *with* walking breaks

Most of you who have time goals will record a faster time, as this gentleman did, if you take the walk breaks early and often.

A friend of mine in his late 40s had been trying for years to run a 3:30 marathon and should have done it, but 3:40 was as fast as he could run. His 5K and 10K performances predicted about 3:25, and he had done plenty of intense training in three different marathon campaigns, including high mileage, lots of speedwork, two runs a day, etc.

Finally, he sent in his entry form for my program, only after I told him that if he didn't run below 3:30 in his goal marathon, I'd return his check. Never did I mention the walk breaks because I knew he would say something about 'sissy stuff' and not sign up.

I knew that in the past he had been physically trained (probably overtrained) for his goal and mainly needed to run with a group to slow down his pace on the long one. The group support during speed sessions also helped him enjoy doing mile repeats for the first time in his life.

After the first session he came up to me, irate, and demanded his money back. 'I can't do these walk breaks: they're sissy stuff!' I refused to return his check, reminding him that a deal was a deal.

He went through the program, complaining during just about every walk break. Secretly, he told friends in his pace group that he wasn't going to walk during the marathon itself.

On marathon morning, his group leader lined up with him and physically restrained him for one minute each mile...walking. At 18 miles, he looked at my friend and said 'Well, you seem to have just enough life in your legs so run along now!' And he did.

His time was 3:25. He had run 15 minutes faster than he had ever run!

At first, he couldn't believe that he could improve that much while walking every mile. But when he analyzed where he had slowed down in past marathons, it was always in the last six to eight miles. In his recent marathon he kept picking up the pace after 18 and knocked five minutes off his pace in that final segment. He finally admitted that the early and regular 'muscle shifts' left his legs feeling strong and responsive all the way to the finish line.

37

WALK/SHUFFLE BREAK QUESTIONS

"SHOULD I CHANGE MY BREAK RATIO DURING THE EVENT?"

If you're feeling good at 9 to 10 miles in the half or 18 to 22 miles in the full, you could stretch the run segments to one additional minute (i.e., from running four minutes and walking one minute, you could extend to running five minutes and walking one minute). After 11 miles in the half or 22 miles in the full, you could stretch another minute or take out the walk breaks entirely. While it's your choice, most who are feeling good keep at least a 30-second break every mile. If you're having a bad day, however, the sooner you can increase the frequency of walk breaks or walk more during each break, the less you will tend to slow down at the end of the event.

"IF I'VE NEVER TRIED THE WALK BREAKS IN TRAINING RUNS, WOULD YOU ADVISE TAKING THEM IN THE EVENT?"

They will only help you. I've received hundreds of letters, faxes, emails and calls from those who heard about the walk break concept the evening before the marathon and tried it the next day. Their response is very similar to this one:

"When I heard you recommend walk breaks at the seminar before the marathon, I didn't want to think about it. I don't know why but it just seemed demeaning for a real runner like me to walk like that. You see, I've run 10 marathons with a personal best of 3:57 and have been proud of the fact that I've never walked.

"But after thinking about it overnight, I decided to prove you wrong by doing exactly what you suggested. To tell you the honest truth, I'd been sick for the last couple of weeks or so and calculated that I probably couldn't run a personal best anyway.

"I walked for a minute every mile and ran my original goal pace for a 3:55 finish during the running portions.

"By the first half of the marathon I was behind my goal pace by three minutes. Aha, I said to myself, Galloway is going to be wrong. If I'm already three minutes behind at the half, I'll be way behind at the finish.

"At 20 miles, I was beginning to feel stronger than I had ever felt at that stage of the marathon. I cut out the walk breaks and ran to the finish, except for short breaks at water stops. While tired during the last six miles, I felt good and passed a lot of people, not really aware of my pace.

"I couldn't believe my time at the finish: 3:52—five minutes faster than I had ever run in my life...and after a bad cold! How did that happen?"

"ARE YOU SAYING THAT I CAN BENEFIT FROM A BREAK—EVEN THOUGH I'M TRAINING FOR A SUB-THREE HOUR MARATHON?"

Yes, I've heard from over 100 runners who broke three hours by taking walk breaks when they couldn't do so by running continuously. A growing number of runners have run below 2:50 by taking walk breaks at least during the first 18 miles. Everyone benefits from walk breaks. They reduce the pounding, allow for water consumption, and speed up recovery from long runs. Competitive runners can erase enough fatigue during the first half so that they can race the second half. The demands of a time goal program require quick recovery, which walk breaks allow. In two to seven days, you can be recovered enough from a 26 to 28 mile training session to do speed training—by going at least two minutes per mile slower than you could go that same distance on that day and taking liberal walk/shuffle breaks from the beginning of the long one.

"DO I HAVE TO TAKE WALK/ SHUFFLE BREAKS AT THE END OF MY RUNS IF MY LEGS ARE TIGHTENING UP?"

Take them as long as you can because they will speed your recovery. If your legs cramp up later during walk breaks then just shuffle through the breaks (by keeping your feet low to the ground with a short stride). At the end, you want to stay as fluid as you can while still alternating the use of the

muscle groups. Cramping at the end tells you to start slower in the next long one and to avoid dehydration the day before, the morning of and during the workout.

"DO I NEED TO TAKE WALK BREAKS ON THE SHORT RUNS DURING THE WEEK?"

If you can run continuously now on shorter midweek runs, you don't have to take the walk breaks. If you want to take them, do so. Walk breaks on midweek runs will insure that you recover faster from the long ones.

WALKING QUESTION: HOW DO I TELL IF I'VE BEEN TAKING SHUFFLE BREAKS OFTEN ENOUGH?

If you are slowing down at the end of your long walks or experiencing a long recovery, try more frequent shuffle breaks from the beginning. *See the next chapter for more information.*

39

WALKING FORM
AND "SHUFFLING"

Most people walk correctly when they use a gentle and comfortable walking motion. But every year, there are exercisers who get injured because they are walking in a way that aggravates some area of the foot or leg. Most of these problems come from trying to walk too fast, with too long a stride or from using a race walk or power walk technique (which I don't recommend).

1. *Avoid a long walking stride.* Maintain a relaxed motion that does not stress the knees, tendons or muscles of the leg, feet, knees or hips. If you feel pain or aggravation in these areas, shorten your stride. Many walkers find that they can walk fairly fast with a short stride. When in doubt, walk more slowly and gently.

2. *Don't lead with your arms.* Minimal arm swing is best. Swinging the arms too much can encourage a longer walk stride which can result in aches and pains. The extra rotation of knees, hips, etc., can lead to longer recovery or injury. The legs should set the rhythm for your walk, allowing you to get into a delightful pattern of right brain thoughts that some call "the zone."

3. *Let your feet move the way that is natural for them.* When walkers try

unnatural techniques that supposedly increase stride length by landing further back on the heel or pushing further on the toe than the legs are designed to move, many get injured. I don't recommend race walking or power walking for this reason.

4. *Walking sticks?* Many long distance walkers have enjoyed using this European import, which gives the hands and arms "something to do." These adapted ski poles have hand grips that are molded to the human hand for secure gripping. On tough terrain, they may aid in balance. On flat terrain, the poles lightly touch the ground. When pesky dogs appear, you have a means of defense. In races, however, they may cause other walkers or runners to stumble and fall.

"SHUFFLING IS BARELY MOVING YOUR FEET AND LEGS, TO LET THE WALKING MUSCLES RECOVER."

Most of the time you're doing it right if you feel comfortable, aren't huffing and puffing and don't have any aches or pains after your first 10 minutes of walking. You are the captain of your walking ship, and it is you who determines how far, how fast, how much you will walk, etc. If you choose to insert shuffle breaks from the beginning of any walk that is long for you, you will gain a major degree of control over fatigue, aches and pains.

WHAT IS A "SHUFFLE"?

With your feet next to the ground, use a short stride with minimal movement. You're still moving forward but not having to spend much energy doing so. When you insert 30 to 60 seconds of shuffling into a regular walk, every two to four minutes, your walking muscles relax and rest. This lowers the chance of aches and pains due to the constant use of the muscles, tendons, etc.

SHUFFLE BEFORE YOU GET TIRED

Most of us, even when untrained, can walk for several miles before fatigue sets in, because walking is an activity that we are bio-engineered to do for hours. Many beginners get discouraged, however, because during the first session or two they don't feel that they are going as far as they should—and add a mile or two. During the extra mileage they often feel strong and hardly tired. In a day or two, they know otherwise as overused muscles complain.

The continuous use of the walking muscles and tendons—even when the walking pace feels completely comfortable—increases stress on our "weak links," increasing aches and pains much more quickly. If you shuffle before your walking muscles start to get tired, you recover instantly. This increases your capacity for exercise while reducing the chance of a next-day soreness attack.

A STRATEGY THAT GIVES YOU CONTROL

You can't wait until you're tired—you must insert the "shuffles" from the beginning. In setting up a conservative strategy of walk/

shuffle, you gain control over fatigue, soreness and aches. Using this fatigue-reduction tool early gives you muscle strength and mental confidence to the end. Even when you don't need the extra muscle strength and resiliency bestowed by the method, you will feel better during and after your walk and will finish knowing that you could have gone further, while recovering faster.

Shuffle breaks allow you a chance to enjoy every walk. By taking them early and often, you can feel strong, even after covering a distance that is very long for you. There is no need to be exhausted at the end of a walk if you insert enough shuffle breaks, for you, on that day.

A SHORT AND VERY GENTLE SHUFFLE

During the shuffle you are only slightly moving your feet and legs. This allows the tendons, muscles, etc. to recover from your regular walking motion. Keep the feet next to the ground, taking baby steps, barely moving the legs.

NO NEED TO EVER ELIMINATE THE SHUFFLE BREAKS

Some beginners assume that they must work toward the day when they don't have to take any shuffle breaks at all. This is up to the individual but is not recommended. Remember that you decide what ratio of walk-shuffle to use. I suggest that you adjust the ratio to how you feel on a given day.

Even the most experienced walker has a few "weak links" that are irritated from continuous use. Shuffling can manage these—or eliminate them.

HOW TO KEEP TRACK OF THE SHUFFLE BREAKS

There are several watches which can be set to beep when it's time to shuffle and then beep again when it's time to walk. Check my website (www.jeffgalloway.com) or a good running store for advice in this area.

HOW TO USE SHUFFLE BREAKS

1. Beginners could walk for 2 minutes and shuffle for 30 seconds. If you feel good during and after the walk, continue with this ratio. If not, adjust the ratio until you feel good.

2. Shuffle breaks allow the body to warm up more easily. If your legs feel tight or you have some soreness, walk for a minute and shuffle for 20-30 seconds—for the first 10 minutes. As the legs loosen up, reduce the shuffles as necessary.

3. On walks longer than 45 minutes or so, even experienced walkers find that a 30-second shuffle, after about 4 minutes of walking, helps recovery and reduces aches and pains.

4. On any given day, when you need more shuffling, do so. Don't ever be afraid to drop back to make the walk more fun and less tiring.

5. The earlier you start the shuffles, the more benefit.

FOOD AND FAT-BURNING

FAT-BURNING AS A WAY OF LIFE

"After seven marathons in five years, I've lost 35 pounds and kept it off. I must say, however, that I was disappointed that I didn't lose a single pound while training for my first one."

If running/walking is one of the very best ways to burn fat, then why do so few half/full marathoners lose weight—at least in their first campaign? Among the many good answers to this one is that a novice should reduce mileage and other stresses to arrive at the starting line and the finish line injury-free. The low mileage associated with this insurance policy will not burn much fat off the body.

Significant dietary changes usually disrupt your metabolism, cause an inconsistent mental focus and lead to energy surges and withdrawals. Other problems encountered by those who change diet and train for a half or full marathon at the same time are the following: stress fractures, nutritional deficiencies and blood sugar level reductions. All can leave you unmotivated to exercise. It's no wonder that we see a lot of program dropouts among those who radically change their diets.

After crossing that finish line for the first time, you're free to set up a five-year plan for making nutritional changes.

But first, let's look into the, unfortunately, expanding world of fat. To better understand how to take it off, we'll look first at how it goes on and the powerful biological instincts that try to keep it in storage. After a good look at the income side, we'll focus on the long-term ways of burning it off as a lifestyle. Once you transform yourself into a fat-burning organism, you'll feel better all day long as you burn more fat.

FAT AS FUEL

Our "set point" determines how much we store

*T*he human organism is lazy. With a primary mission of survival, each of us is programmed to slowly build up extra fat storage. For millions of years, this has been a proven "insurance policy," which allowed our ancient ancestors to survive through periods of starvation and sickness. The mechanisms of fat storage, described below, support a well-established principle called "set point." This powerful regulatory mechanism increases your appetite for weeks or months, after periods of fat loss due to reduced calorie intake, illness, and even psychological deprivation. Unfortunately, it does its job too well, leaving you fatter than you were before the fat loss. Understanding how the set point works as your hedge against starvation is the most important step in learning how to adjust it downward, or at least manage it, for the rest of your life.

WHAT IS FAT?

When you eat a pat of butter, you might as well inject it onto your thigh or stomach. While dietary fat is directly deposited, protein and carbohydrates (even sugar) will be converted into fat only when you've consumed too many calories from those sources throughout the day. If you're trying to reduce the fat blanket, it helps to eat complex carbohydrates (baked potatoes, rice, whole grains, vegetables) and lean protein sources (legumes, turkey breast, nonfat dairy products, etc.).

AN UNLIMITED SUPPLY OF THE BEST FUEL FOR RUNNING AND WALKING

Only body fat is used as fuel, not the fat in your diet. It is an excellent energy source, leaving a small amount of waste product, which is easily removed through the increased blood flow of exercise. While stored sugar is limited, you can't go far enough to use up your fat storage. Even a 140-pound person with the unusually low level of two percent body fat has hundreds of miles of fuel on board.

ANOTHER DIFFERENCE BETWEEN MEN AND WOMEN

Men tend to store fat on the surface of the body, often on the outside of the stomach area. Most females store fat internally at first. Thousands of areas between muscle cells are filled up first. Many young women feel that some dramatic change has occurred around the age of 30 when they suddenly start showing fat accumulation on the outside of their bodies, while maintaining the same diet and level of exercise.

Note: For more info on fat-burning, see Jeff's books Half Marathon *and* Walking, *www.JeffGalloway.com.*

They've actually been storing fat inside for many years. Once the inner areas are filled, women notice a dramatic change on the outside of their thighs or stomachs, often in less than a year.

THE SET POINT IS PROGRAMMED TO INCREASE YOUR FAT ACCUMULATION, SLIGHTLY, EACH YEAR

By the time humans enter their mid-20s, most have settled into an accustomed level of calorie-burning and calorie consumption. Your set point is adjusted for the amount of fat you've collected to that point. Very slowly, your basal metabolism rate (the calories which are burned each day to keep you alive, doing routine activities) is reduced. Since your appetite doesn't adjust downward very quickly, most humans consume a few more calories than they need, each week, producing a slow increase in fat accumulation. The internal set point quickly adjusts to the higher level of fat, as the new "set point." Increased fat levels are biologically reinforced with each additional year of age as fat helps one survive a prolonged illness or other major interruption of health or food intake.

DIETS DON'T WORK BECAUSE THEY READJUST THE METABOLISM "THERMOSTAT" IN THE WRONG DIRECTION

By depriving yourself of food, you can reduce your body fat temporarily as you reduce your metabolism rate and your motivation to exercise. As soon as the diet is over, however, your set point mechanism unleashes a starvation reflex that keeps you eating until the fat levels are slightly higher than they were before the diet. At the same time, your metabolism rate stays low to help you store fat more quickly. No matter how mentally focused you are, you'll find yourself with more fat on your frame when you mess with that very powerful survival mechanism.

THE STARVATION REFLEX

By now you know that diets are read by your intuitive set point mechanism as a form of starvation, planting a future seed for increased fat storage. Over millions of years, our ancient ancestors withstood regular famines, establishing very complex and quick reactions to prepare for even the possibility of food reduction. If you're getting food in adequate quantity and frequency, your system doesn't feel the need to store fat. But the reflex starts into action when you've waited too long between snacks or meals on any day. The longer you wait to eat your next food, the more you stimulate the fat-depositing enzymes. When you eat your next food, more of it will be processed into fat. But that's not all of the bad news. A longer wait between meals increases your appetite, which leads to overeating—during the next meal or over the next few hours. Even if you've eaten three to five times a day but have eaten too few calories for that day's activities, you'll experience an increased appetite during the next 12 to 36 hours.

45

PSYCHOLOGICAL STARVATION

The negative power of the subconscious mind will crush your attempts to restrict your food intake. Almost everyone feels guilty about eating certain delicious items that tend to put fat on our bodies due to fat, sugar content or quantity. If you tell yourself that next week (or next month) you're going to go on a diet that will really get the fat off your body, you give yourself a license to overeat calories and decadent foods, quickly, before the diet begins. Not only does this make your fat reduction task more difficult, but it often results in a steady delay in the start date of the perceived austere diet.

Depriving yourself of one or more foods that you dearly love will start a psychological time bomb ticking away. Yes, you can tell yourself that you'll never eat another doughnut, hamburger, french fry, etc. You may even be able to abstain for an extended period of time. But at some point in the future, when the food is around and no one else is, your starvation reflex will grab hold of you in a binge. Over time, the binges will lead you to consume more of that decadent food than you deprived yourself of during the period of prohibition.

True Confessions: An Ice Cream Addiction Is Broken

I've always enjoyed ice cream, but until about 1970 my cravings for it were under control. Then, I discovered Breyer's Chocolate Chip Mint ice cream. At first it was a special treat eaten about once a week, say after a long run or a very hard workout. Gradually, I increased the reward frequency, as I was increasing my daily mileage from 10 miles to as much as 30 miles. I justified the speed it took to empty a half gallon box of my daily reward by the number of extra calories burned on the track, road and trail. It seemed to me then that the supermarkets had installed a super magnet in the frozen food section and my shopping cart was pulled there almost under its own power. In the mid-1980s, as my wife, Barb, and I celebrated our tenth anniversary, we were determined to improve our diets. Knowing that our almost daily dose of the smooth, light-tasting ice cream couldn't be good for our arteries, we made an austere New Year's resolution: no more Breyer's ice cream.

For two years we survived the "cold turkey" diet. Then, one fateful day, we held a birthday party at our house, and some well meaning friend brought over a box of the banned substance. Both Barb and I did well during the party, but during the cleanup the box was melting on the counter with only a little left. We jointly decided that one spoonful wouldn't kill us. The taste brought back the submerged cravings, which had been there all along. I'm sure we ate more Breyer's Chocolate Chip Mint in the next six months than we had deprived ourselves of over the two-year prohibition.

At that point, I decided to try a five-year moderation plan. I visualized myself five years in the future, eating a bowl of that ice cream every fifth night and being completely satisfied. Somewhat understanding the psychological starvation with which I had shocked my system, I kept telling myself that the ice cream would always be available if I wanted it more often. When things got tough and I felt deprived, I gave into a bowl, while visualizing that in five to six years, even with it in the freezer, I only wanted to eat it every fifth or sixth night.

Continuing to bring the visualization to the present, I saw myself four years hence, eating a bowl of it every three to four nights. Three years from that date, I would enjoy a bowl every two to three nights, and by two years from that time, a bowl every night would satisfy me. You must know that at the starting point, I was consuming about a quart every night.

Each time I got out the ice cream, for the next year, I went through my visualizations for the next five years. I filled in my eating rehearsal with changes in eating frequency—to avoid being so hungry in the evening. Over the years, I filled in these visualizations with an ever-expanding variety of foods that I learned to like but which were much lower in fat.

It worked! Before 60 months had elapsed, I was eating a bowl of full-fat ice cream every sixth night—at the most. Normally, the amount that has been consumed is much less than that. While I have made some integrated changes to my diet, I'm not gloating. I keep telling myself that the Breyer's is in the freezer.

BURNING IT OFF

*B*ig and little things that can burn fat and keep it off

...REGULAR EXERCISE IMPROVES DISEASE RESISTANCE

In the last chapter we talked about the "set point" which regulates your appetite to maintain fat accumulation at a certain level, which gradually increases each five to 10 years. One of the very best and proven ways of readjusting the set point is by doing regular endurance exercise. We're not just talking about increased fat-burning during exercise. The increased health benefits of regular exercise (enhanced resistance to disease, stronger heart, more efficient cardiovascular system, etc.) give intuitive signals to the body that there is lowered risk of long-term health problems, thus reducing the need for increased fat levels. A fit 70-year-old, for example, can often fight off a disease better and quicker than an average (and not very fit) 30-year old. Your set point mechanism seems to have a sensor that intuitively monitors long-term trends in your body. In most cases, the set point is adjusted higher in those who suffer a series of health setbacks. In combination with regular exercise, however, it's possible to lower the monitored fat level. Let's look at some of the many reasons why exercise controls fat buildup.

...BY BURNING OFF THAT PIECE OF PIE

Regular running and walking keeps fat off the body, burning off excess calories. Most beginners experience some fat burn-off, even when their weight stays the same, particularly when diet is not dramatically increased. If you've consumed more calories than you've burned during a given day, you can literally burn them off with an after-dinner walk or jog. This is particularly helpful if you've consumed excess calories from carbohydrates on a given day.

...BY BURNING MORE FAT WHEN WE'RE ASLEEP

Running/walking regularly for more than 45 minutes (even with walk and shuffle breaks) trains our exercising muscle cells to be fat-burners at all times of the night and day. After months of regular distance exercise, you will have transformed a vast number of running muscle cells into fat-burners which prefer fat as a fuel, even when sitting around all day or when asleep at night. Long ones which exceed 90 minutes, when done every two to three weeks, speed up the transformation of the muscle cells from sugar-burners to fat-burners.

Note: See Jeff's books Half Marathon *and* Walking *for more fatburning information (www.JeffGalloway.com).*

SUGAR-BURNING PRODUCES WASTE BUILDUP—SO SLOW DOWN!

Glycogen is the form of sugar that is stored in the muscles for quick energy. Not only is this the fuel that gets us started, but it sustains us for the first half hour of exercise. Unfortunately, when this form of sugar is used for strenuous exercise, it leaves behind a lot of waste product. Going even a little too fast at the beginning depletes valuable glycogen quicker as it fills up the muscles and slows them down. This is why many runners/walkers don't feel great during the first few miles of a workout. The faster the starting pace, the more uncomfortable we'll feel. Most of this discomfort can be eliminated with a slow start and more frequent or longer early walk breaks - in short, a better warmup. But there will be still more waste produced from glycogen than that experienced when burning fat.

48

The supply of glycogen is very limited, and it is necessary for brain function. A small amount of this "muscle sugar" is burned every mile, even after you've shifted primarily into fat-burning. So it's very important on long runs to conserve this resource by keeping the pace very slow from the beginning. When supplies run low, your "energy control" will hold back enough for your most crucial organ and force a breakdown of fat and protein—a very uncomfortable process. You'll avoid this negative effect by gradually increasing your distance, by putting in more walk/shuffle breaks from the beginning, and by exercising at least three days a week (regularity of exercise).

FROM 15-45 MINUTES, YOUR MUSCLES GRADUALLY SHIFT INTO FAT-BURNING

Your body must not believe that you're really going out for a long one until you keep moving forward for more than a quarter hour. At this point, you begin to break down body fat for fuel (dietary fat is converted directly into body fat and is not burned for energy). It takes some work to break down the "excess baggage" on your body into free fatty acids and triglycerides that can keep you going mile after mile. If you continue exercising longer than about 15 minutes at a pace that is within your capacity, you start shifting into fat-burning. As your exercise continues past the quarter-hour mark, you start a transition into fat-burning as long as you continue to exercise at a level of exertion that is within your capacity.

IF YOU'RE STILL EXERCISING COMFORTABLY AFTER 45 MINUTES, YOU'LL BE BURNING ALMOST EXCLUSIVELY FAT AS FUEL

By starting at a slow pace and taking walk breaks as needed, you can lower your exertion level enough to stay in the fat-burning zone for an extended time. This conserves glycogen for later use as you burn off the extra blanket around your stomach or thighs.

UNTRAINED MUSCLES MUST LEARN HOW TO BURN FAT

Those who are not in shape for endurance activity must train the muscles to burn fat. Beginning exercisers may have to walk until they get up to an hour or more of continuous activity. Instead of walk/shuffle breaks, some totally out-of-shape beginners need to take one to two minute "sit down" breaks every five to eight minutes to stay in the fat-burning zone. After a few weeks, however, most of these novices can improve to continuous 45 to 60-minute walks at a steady pace. At that point, they may increase the walking or hold the distance steady and/or add jogging breaks. See the "Run-Walk-Run" chapter for specific guidance in this area. Some people take longer to progress. Everyone needs to exercise patience.

SLOW AEROBIC EXERCISE BURNS FAT; FAST ANAEROBIC EXERCISE BURNS SUGAR

Fat can only be burned in the muscle cell when there's an adequate supply of oxygen. This is "aerobic exercise": exertions that are done at an easy enough pace so that the blood can provide all of the oxygen needed by the muscles. As soon as you increase the pace beyond your current capacity or go farther than your muscles are trained to go, the running or walking muscles can't get enough oxygen to burn fat and shift back to the readily available but inefficient energy source, glycogen. You're now "anaerobic," meaning that the muscles aren't getting enough oxygen. The longer and faster you exercise anaerobically, the worse you'll feel and the sooner you'll quit because of waste product accumulation. *(See* Galloway's Book on Running *and* Walking *for a more detailed explanation. JeffGalloway.com)*

WALK OR SHUFFLE BREAKS AND A SLOW START PACE KEEP YOU IN THE FAT-BURNING ZONE LONGER

Not only does an easy pace from the start reduce the waste product buildup in the first quarter hour, it pushes back your wall. If you're used to going five miles, slowing the pace about two minutes per mile and

adding more walk or shuffle breaks can get you to seven to nine miles feeling the same way you felt after five. I'm not recommending that you make this type of an increase every run for it's always better to gradually increase your mileage. A slower pace with more walk/shuffle breaks will allow you to do this with little or no risk of injury or overfatigue. The extra mileage means that you are burning more calories and fat.

LONG WORKOUTS TRAIN YOUR MUSCLE CELLS TO BE FAT-BURNING FURNACES

The continuous movement of the body during long, slow ones mobilizes an incredible number of muscle cells in the legs, back, butt and related areas. By slowly covering several miles, three times a week, this network of muscles specializes in the work that can keep moving the body in the most efficient way. Since fat is the most efficient and abundant fuel, the muscles will adapt to become fat-burners if this over 45-minute run/walk is done regularly enough.

The adaptation to fat-burning is more difficult for those who've done little or no exercise before. The same fat-burning process works for you as it does for world class athletes. You may not notice it for a while because the changes are going on inside the muscle cells. Keep telling yourself "I'm becoming a fat-burning furnace" because you are!

THE MORE 45+MINUTE EXERCISE SESSIONS, THE MORE EFFECTIVE THE FAT METABOLISM CHANGE

By slowing down enough to surpass the 45-minute barrier, you show your body that you're serious about endurance. It responds by changing the former sugar-burning cells

49

into fat-burners. The minimum necessary is one 45+ minute session per week (but the process is put into "fast forward" by going 90 minutes+ every two weeks. As the long one increases significantly in a half or full marathon program, you force more and more cells into the more efficient mode of fat metabolism and keep them there.

REGULARITY IS VERY IMPORTANT

To maintain the capacity of your expanding fat furnace, you'll need at least two other 30-minute sessions a week. If these can be increased to at least 45 minutes, you'll improve the adaptation. It's better to slow down from the beginning of exercise so that you'll feel better, be more motivated to continue, and go further.

RAISING YOUR CORE BODY TEMPERATURE CAN TRIGGER FAT BURN-OFF

50 Running and walking elevates your core body temperature. Many experts believe that this produces a healthy "fever" which often kills off infections before they cause colds or worse. But the greater your blanket of body fat, the more heat you'll retain, which can lead to excessive fluid loss through sweating. Your body's temperature control mechanism will try to reduce this source of stress if you run and walk regularly. After months of regular long runs or walks, you'll program yourself to burn off the blanket, reducing your set point and body fat.

IT'S COUNTER-PRODUCTIVE TO DRAMATICALLY INCREASE YOUR DISTANCE QUICKLY

Humans often want changes to occur too rapidly. If a little exercise burns x amount of fat, it's tempting to log twice as many miles to double your fat-burning. This doesn't work. By adding too much distance, too

soon, you'll get tired or injured, forcing you to stop exercising or cut back dramatically. Even worse is the possibility that you'll get mentally burned out. If you continue to go slowly and increase total weekly mileage by no more than 10 percent, you'll reduce your chance of injury and burn-out to almost nothing.

THE START IS CRUCIAL

The biggest mistake exercisers make is starting too hard, too fast. This is so easy to do because it usually doesn't feel too hard, but six to 10 minutes later you're wishing that you were finished. By forcing yourself to start much more slowly than you want, you'll receive a stream of benefits, speeding your entry into the fat zone and setting yourself up for more enjoyment later. The slower you go at the start, the easier it will be at the end to increase distance. Slow starts also speed up your recovery, which will improve your motivation to get out there for the next one.

WHY DIDN'T I LOSE WEIGHT DURING MY TRAINING PROGRAMS?

Don't use the scales as your gauge of fat loss. You've probably lost fat, even though your weight stays the same. While fat is burned during your workouts, there are other physiological changes which will increase your body weight in a healthy way, helping you to improve exercise performance. More water and glycogen is stored in the muscle cells so that you can stay cooler and maintain energy during exercise. Blood volume also increases when you do regular endurance exercise to more easily supply the exercising muscles with oxygen and nutrients. All three of these changes increase body weight in a good way, preparing you for easier and better training.

IT'S NOT A GOOD IDEA TO TRY TO LOSE A LOT OF WEIGHT WHILE TRAINING FOR A HALF OR FULL MARATHON

A four to six-month endurance program produces enough lifestyle challenges without adding the stress of a diet change. To accomplish your goal, you need a steady flow of energy. When you're strenuously training while on a diet, the energy supply is often interrupted, resulting in low motivation and negative feelings during and after exercise.

When gearing up the body to go 13 or 26 miles, I want you to focus on three items:

1. Incorporating regular endurance exercise into your lifestyle,

2. Building the endurance necessary to go the distance, and

3. Learning how to enjoy the process so you'll want to do it again.

If you try to change diet during this mission, you're very likely to suffer from confused priorities. It's so easy to think you're eating healthier foods while you omit certain nutrients needed for performance. Unfortunately, the loss of these nutritional building blocks isn't noticed until weeks or months later when you're dragging around—unmotivated to exercise.

Unless you had nutritional problems before the program started, stick with the diet that you've been using. Certainly it's okay to divide up your food into more small meals a day *(see next chapter)* and to reduce fat intake a little, but don't make any radical changes. If you feel that you have some nutritional problems at any time, see a sports nutritionist, especially one that has had success in working with long distance athletes.

During a half or full marathon program it's okay to say "I'm starting my diet later"... after the event.

51

HOW YOU EAT DETERMINES HOW GOOD YOU FEEL... AND HOW MUCH FAT YOU STORE

THE INCOME SIDE OF THE LEDGER

"I love being able to eat all day long, while losing five pounds in four months." A successful eating plan is one which provides all essential nutrients, allows you to maintain a good energy level for exercise and for daily activities, while maintaining the body fat level with which you feel comfortable. For fat level management, you must stay in touch with the principles of your set point and be honest with yourself. This means balancing what you want to look like with the type of eating plan you're willing to follow, not for a month or so, but as a lifestyle. Most successful dietary changes are small ones, which allow you to feel good all day long so that you can exercise and burn off the pounds of fat you want to lose.

The primary purpose of this chapter is to help you set up an eating plan that will give you sufficient energy for your daily activities as well as long distance training. Fat-burning should be a longer term activity and integrated into lifestyle, taking a back seat to the establishment of exercise as the prime mover in your personal wellness program.

So exercise burns the fat, is the furnace that keeps it off, and gives you the good attitude and the reason to continue working toward your goal. Just knowing that you're burning it off gives purpose to your dietary changes. But it works both ways. Your eating plan can give you the energy you need to be motivated to exercise as it delivers the nutrients for muscle exertion and repair. Most runners and walkers find that only a few changes in eating frequency and food choices make the difference in keeping off the baggage that they worked so hard to get rid of.

The primary mission of eating is to give you the essential nutrients with a steady metabolism boost so that you can maintain a motivational level of blood sugar to do all of life's activities. Your energy level is somewhat determined by what you eat and significantly influenced by how much and how often you eat.

Note: For more information on the topics in this chapter, see Jeff's books Half Marathon *and* Walking *(www.JeffGalloway.com).*

Eating all day long!

Yes, it's better for fat control and your energy level if you eat every two to three hours. Our human digestion system was designed for grazing: taking in modest amounts of food all day long. Each time we eat, even small amounts, our digestive system gears up to process the nutrients and dispose of the bulk. This means that you're burning calories for an extended period beyond the eating of the snack—in order to digest the food.

On the other hand, the starvation reflex kicks into fat-depositing when your metabolism slows down. Even if you wait three hours to eat, you'll increase the fat-depositing enzymes so that more of the next meal becomes fat. To prevent starvation, you have an intuitive mechanism that conserves resources and adds fat to the body if you're not grazing regularly.

The longer you go without food, the more your metabolism will shut down into a fasting or low level of energy. If you're not eating enough food, "metabolism control" will cut your flow of energy so that you don't burn up your reserve. The longer you fast, the more likely you will want to be sedentary and resist moving around. So if you're trying to exercise in the afternoon, five hours after your last meal or snack, your metabolism controller will probably be steering you toward the couch instead of the track or trail.

Small meals energize; big meals put you to sleep

Your digestive system gears up whenever there is any food consumed. A small to moderate snack will give you a significant metabolism increase and can be processed efficiently. A big meal will take a while to process. Your metabolism gears up to process it, but so many resources are needed (especially blood supply) that your body organism wants to shut down other activities to process the bulk in your extended gastrointestinal complex. This is why you feel sleepy and unmotivated about half an hour after a big meal.

What you eat makes a difference

A good balance of fresh, complex carbohydrates along with some protein and a little fat will leave you satisfied for an extended period after eating. Too much food, too much sugar and starch, and too much fat in a meal will lead to fat accumulation.

Carbohydrates give you the energy you need in a form the body can easily use. Complex carbohydrates (such as vegetables, fruits, whole grain products, legumes, etc.) have fiber and various other nutrients neatly packaged with the energy. The more fiber, the longer you'll feel satisfied afterward because it takes the body a longer time to process the food. Simple carbohydrates (sugar, starch, etc.) are broken down so fast that you can consume a great quantity of calories without feeling satisfied. Excess calories that accumulate during a day are processed into fat when they haven't been needed for energy for several hours.

Fat is directly deposited on your body—you might as well inject it to your stomach or thigh. A little fat in each snack or meal will keep you from being hungry for a longer period. But once the fat content exceeds about 25 percent of the calories, particularly in a meal, you'll be storing significant quantities. Since fat slows down digestion, you'll be more uncomfortable if you want to exercise too soon after eating. The more fat you eat, the more lethargic you will feel.

53

*E*ven an energy bar, eaten an hour before exercise with a glass of water, will raise my blood sugar level to workout motivation levels. It's still better, however, to eat snacks all day long, instead of waiting until you feel extremely hungry.

Eating fat after exercise also slows down your restocking of glycogen. Studies have shown that a high carbohydrate meal within 30 to 120 minutes after a run/walk will help you re-stock the vital energy supply you need for the first 15 to 30 minutes of exercise. When too much fat is consumed, the glycogen is not replenished and you don't feel very good as you start each successive workout.

Sugar and starch are simple carbohydrates which are processed so quickly that you usually get hungry before you've even had a chance to burn them off. Since we tend to follow our hunger, eating meals with sugar and starch almost always leads to more calories consumed in a 24-hour period than we are burning off. Excess calories are transformed into body fat. A small amount of simple carbohydrates is okay—especially if it's a food that you dearly love. So don't prevent yourself from eating that piece of pizza; just enforce the one-slice rule.

Protein is the building block of our muscles. We need some each day to replace the normal wear and tear of our muscles and other tissue. By eating some protein with each of your snacks, you'll prolong your feeling of satisfaction—extending the time before you feel hungry. You can certainly eat too much protein. If your total consumption of calories during a day is more than you've burned up, the excess will be converted into fat—whether the surplus comes from carbs, protein, fat or all of the above. Too much protein in the diet can cause other health problems. Most nutritionists I've interviewed have told me that even a steady diet of 30

percent or more of protein can lead to kidney damage.

Fiber will also keep you from getting hungry for a while. Many types of soluble fiber, such as oat bran, coat the lining of the stomach, slowing down the release of sugars into the bloodstream. Practically any fiber that is in a food will increase the feeling of satisfaction. A baked potato, for example, leaves me satisfied about three times as long as an apple, when each has the same number of calories. The baked potato fiber is much more complex than that found in apples, and the latter has much more sugar. When you substitute an apple for a piece of pie or a bowl of ice cream, you reduce calories and fat.

BLOOD SUGAR LEVEL (BSL)

Your motivation (to exercise, to work, to play with the kids, etc.) will also vary with the level of sugar in your blood. If you have too little, you'll tend to be lazy and sleepy and will find it difficult to concentrate on anything. But if there's too much sugar in the food you eat, your blood sugar level will rise quickly and make you feel very good for a short while...and then crash. An elevated BSL will trigger a release of insulin, which does two negative things. It sends the BSL lower than it was before you ate your snack or meal. But insulin is also the chemical that promotes fat storage so it starts to process that excess energy into your storage areas. Eating all day long helps to maintain a moderately elevated BSL (but not too high) and maximizes the chance that you'll feel motivated and energized to be more active in everything you do.

COMPLEX CARBOHYDRATES GIVE YOU A DISCOUNT RATE

The more complex the fiber in a food, the more calories are burned in the processing of that food. Take a baked potato, for example. If you eat the skin and all, you'll be burning up to 25 percent of the calories to process it. Contrast this with the fact that virtually 100 percent of the fat calories in french fries, for example, are directly deposited on your body.

A GRACE PERIOD

Even if you eat too many calories in carbohydrates and protein, you can still go out for a walk or jog and burn them off. Here's another way to gain control over your weight and fat level.

Boosting Blood Sugar— And Motivation

"Eating during my race allowed me to mentally feel great after the marathon and celebrate with my friends all evening."

Counterattacking low blood sugar level on long ones

Even if your BSL is ideal at the beginning of a workout, it is certain to be dramatically reduced as you push your limits beyond 15 miles (and many runners experience the "crash" before this). Almost everyone will suffer low blood sugar at the end of these sessions if he or she does not eat quality carbohydrate snacks before the start and during the second half of the long one.

BLOOD SUGAR BOOSTERS

Even the most conditioned exerciser will suffer a blood sugar drop when he or she goes more than about 10 miles. The only way to win this battle and boost the BSL is to counterattack. Whether you use energy bars or other foods, here are the principles which have led to blood sugar success:

1. Choose a food that is low in fat (less than 10 percent of the total calories of the food in fat) but which contains significant soluble fiber.

2. If the food is a solid, like energy bars, be sure to drink at least four ounces of water for every 100 calories of the food.

3. Cut the solid food up into small pieces for easier consumption during the second half of the long distance workout.

4. Drink water with each piece.

5. Test your eating routine during long training sessions to find the right time sequence, quantity, etc. for you.

CHOOSING AND TESTING ENERGY FOOD

There are many foods advertised as sports energizers. As is found in all commercial products, some brands make inflated claims. First, determine what you need from the snack. Next, evaluate the possible products, with the help of knowledgeable running/

walking friends, sports nutritionists or trust-worthy running store staff.

Next, try several of these for long and short distances and choose one or two to fine-tune for the event itself. Use your chosen foods on as many workouts as possible before using them in the half or full marathon.

You and your digestive tract can learn to like just about anything. Don't give up on a food because it doesn't taste good at first or doesn't seem to work for you the first time. Take small amounts of the food with water at first. Over time, you can increase the amount of the food as your systems learn to digest and use it.

ENERGY-BOOSTING CHOICES

• High carbohydrate foods with soluble fiber

Supplying a moderate boost of energy, these products usually deliver a good BSL for an extended period. Be sure to check the label of the product you choose to ensure that it is low in fat (fat calories are less than 10 percent total calories). Eat a portion about one hour before the workout and pieces of the product throughout the second half of the workout—always with water.

• High carbohydrate gels

These thick-but-sweet products have the consistency of paste. They usually deliver a stronger BSL boost at first, which wears off after several minutes. Read and follow the directions on the package, and try them out in training sessions extensively. Because they are somewhat liquid, they

get into the blood stream quicker than the "bar" products, but it is still wise to take water with each packet, if available. Once you start taking these, you must continue consuming them until the end of the workout to avoid blood sugar letdown.

• Fluids with sugar (mostly electrolyte beverages)

While these can be an excellent fluid replacement before and after training runs, the electrolyte beverages tend to send the BSL into a rollercoaster ride when taken in the event itself. Without a substance such as soluble fiber to slow down the absorption of the sugar (and maintain the level), you can easily encourage an insulin reaction by drinking them regularly. If you are desperate and feel the need to drink some of these products, dilute them with water.

• Concentrated carbohydrate fuels

There are several fluids on the market which offer a great amount of carbohydrate in a small bottle. Similar to syrup, these fluids take a while to digest and require fluid from your body to do so. As they will tend to dehydrate you, they are not recommended for drinking either the day before, the morning before, or during the event itself (or during comparable times in training workouts). Their concentration will often cause fat accumulation.

The fluid goes so quickly through your digestive system that you're hungry before you've had a chance to burn off the significant number of calories.

• Hard candies, gummi bears, etc.

One of the most reliable "boosters" is the

inexpensive, little hard candies. Each one of these supplies so few total calories that insulin response is unlikely. If you start eating one about every mile during the second half of the marathon, you will gain some BSL boost.

It's always better to drink water at every stop when taking these candies. In addition, a pre-event snack of quality carbohydrate is recommended to maintain BSL until the halfway point.

Look at the fat content of any exercise snack—and energy bars specifically. It is recommended that you choose bars in which the fat calories comprise less than 10 percent of the total calories. The more fat, the longer it takes for them to be digested, and the more likely it will be that the food will give you a lethargic reaction instead of an energetic one.

58

THE ENDURANCE DIET

*"**A**t first I had stomach trouble on most of my runs. Then I wrote down what I ate the day before and eliminated the problems. I almost never have stomach problems now."*

24 HOURS BEFORE AND 24 HOURS AFTER

If you want to know which pill or snack you can eat to send you zooming to top performance, then get another book. Over my five decades of running, I've heard just about every claim made by a nutritional product, and almost none of them seem to deliver what they promise. While you'll find a listing of foods that will give you energy and reduce gastrointestinal problems later in this chapter, I believe that steady training with rest produces successful performance. Food will give you energy to train and the raw material to rebuild muscle.

Even though North Americans tend to eat a lot of junk food, they generally get enough nutrients during a six-month period to train for and complete a long distance event without incident. But even if you are deficient in some nutritional way as you walk to the starting line, it's too late to do anything about it. Except for the issue of maintaining blood sugar level, noted in this chapter, by that time your nutritional homework has either been done or not.

TRAIN YOUR STOMACH

Just as you must train your legs to go the distance, your digestive system must be fine-tuned to deliver the nutrients under the stress of long ones. In this process, you'll steadily eliminate (or adjust the intake of) foods that produce negative effects. You want to get into a routine, knowing exactly what to eat, when to eat it, how much to drink with it, etc. If you adjust this during your series of long ones, you'll reduce the chance of problems in the event to almost nothing. Your stomach and GI tract can adapt to delivering nutrients with little or no negative reactions throughout a strenuous endurance event.

ELIMINATING PROBLEM FOODS

While a variety of foods is great for overall nutrition, your pre-race diet will be more focused. Analyze your eating the day before and the morning of long ones. Over the months, eliminate foods that cause problems. If you had a problem, eliminate the food or foods that could have caused it. Realize that it may have been the quantity of food. It's better to err on the side of eating too little than eating too much. But, please, don't starve yourself. Continue to eat small meals or snacks (which you know will digest quickly) all day long into the evening.

CONTROL YOUR FOOD DESTINY THE DAY BEFORE WITH A SCHEDULE

Start with the foods that have digested quickly for you leading up to long workouts and didn't cause stomach or other GI problems. Write down the schedule in a journal or notebook where you can review it before your next long one. After each snack, note the amount, the time, and any fluid you consumed with it. As you work on the right quantity and timetable, you'll gain control over how you feel the day before and the morning of the half or full marathon.

Jeff Galloway's Eating Countdown

The following is the most I would ever eat before a race. Usually, I leave out some of the items. This is not meant to be a suggestion for what you should eat. You should set the schedule which works best for you.

The day before the long one

9:00 a.m. Cereal or bagel with lowfat cream cheese, coffee (or tea with orange juice)
Drink 8 ounces OJ or Sports drink

10:30 a.m. Energy bar or whole-grain bagel or baked potato with nonfat cole slaw
Drink 8 ounces of water or sports drink

12:00 noon Grilled chicken sandwich or sliced turkey breast on whole-grain bread, steamed broccoli or spinach salad
Drink 8 ounces of water or sports drink

1:30-2:00 p.m. Energy bar or cereal or baked potato with nonfat sour cream
Drink 8 ounces of water or sports drink

3:30-4:00 p.m. Grilled chicken sandwich or turkey breast burrito with pinto beans and sliced tomatoes, energy bar
Drink 8 ounces of water or sports drink

5:30-6:00 p.m. Baked potato with nonfat sour cream or brown rice with steamed broccoli, energy bar, if hungry
Drink 8 ounces of water

7:00-7:30 p.m. Energy bar
Drink 8 ounces of water

9:00 p.m. Energy bar, if hungry (otherwise, just water)
8 ounces of water

Race morning

5 a.m. Wake up
Drink 8-10 ounces of water

6 a.m. Energy bar, cup of coffee
Drink 4 ounces of water

6:30 a.m. Drink 4-8 ounces of water, if there's no sloshing in the stomach

7:00 a.m. Start Race

60

HYPONATREMIA

There is a potentially serious health problem if your sodium levels are low and you continue to drink beyond the point of being well hydrated. This is called hyponatremia, a life-threatening disruption of the necessary flow of fluids during exercise. The chance of this happening is extremely low, but use your common sense about drinking more when you've been drinking all day long. This condition is aggravated by being on restrictive diets, fasting, being sick and taking medications. Recommendation: 14-27 ounces an hour of water. No more than 27 oz per hour.

SPORTS DRINKS

The electrolyte beverages will help you top off your fluid levels and, to some extent, your glycogen levels. Again, don't go overboard. A maximum of one quart of your favorite sports drink is my recommendation, consumed over the "awake" hours. The Accelerade product has great research behind it.

FOLLOW THE DIET THAT GOT YOU HERE

You'll probably be tempted, after walking through a pre-race expo, to try one of the "miracle foods" that you hear about there. Don't do it! Even if a food is the best in its category, if you haven't used it before, you'll probably have some significant negative reactions. To reduce the chance of food and GI problems, use the same eating plan as on your long runs: the same foods, the same amounts, the same timetable. If you had GI problems, reduce quantity and/ or consult a sports nutritionist. Since you're going to have some nervousness and stress, it doesn't take much of a nutritional change to produce intestinal misery.

EATING DURING THE BIG EVENT FOR BETTER CONCENTRATION AND...CELEBRATION

Your eating plan during the event will give you an amazing amount of control over your attitude at the end and your ability to enjoy your accomplishment afterward. By eating some blood sugar-boosting snacks during long training sessions and the race, you can stay more focused and motivated. Even when your legs are totally fatigued, your spirit can soar if you manage the blood sugar level.

The long ones should serve as the testing ground for your stomach. I eat an energy bar (around 230 calories) before long runs and find that my blood sugar remains stable for eight to10 miles. It doesn't pay to wait until the level goes down to prop it up. About 60 to 90 minutes into a long run or event, start reloading with your snack of choice: energy gels, energy bars, etc. (always with water). If you didn't eat before the start, your blood sugar-boosters should begin at the 10 to 15-minute mark. The frequency and amount of gel or other snacks should be adjusted on long ones so that you know what to do on race day. If you got nauseous at the end of long ones, you probably ate too much at one time, didn't drink enough water, or overloaded the system with a sport drink, etc. Having a blood sugar drop at the end means that you need to increase the amount or frequency of your booster product all the way to the end. It's usually better to take smaller amounts and take them more often.

When the blood sugar stays up, you'll be able to concentrate better, even at the end. You'll not only avoid the concentration loss

61

that accompanies a blood sugar crash at the end but you'll also recover quicker. Such a crash is a major stress on your system and activates your left brain to release a continuous stream of negative messages. A good, stable BSL leaves you feeling under control at the end of the race so you'll want to celebrate afterwards.

If you're one of the few exercisers who have digestive problems with the smallest amount of gel, try gummi bears. Of course, you don't want anything so large that you could choke on it. Sucking on one per mile (with water) has not caused problems for anyone so far.

WATER VS. SPORTS DRINKS

Electrolyte beverages can cause problems in long runs and races. The sugar in the drinks overloads the digestive system, slowing down the absorption of water, which the body needs greatly. Many runners who use sports drinks in long distance events suffer

from nausea during the second half—due to the residue of sports drink fluid which stays there causing trouble.

This differs greatly from the experience of cyclists. In running/walking, the digestive system slows down dramatically—or shuts down completely. Cycling is not stressful enough to shut down digestion, allowing sports drinks to be absorbed. Much of the research on the sports drinks was done on cyclists.

TIME GOAL RUNNERS/WALKERS NEED TO PRACTICE ON LONG ONES AND MILE REPEAT SESSIONS

Everyone should practice "eating on the run" during long ones. During their mile repeat sessions, time goal runners will also benefit from eating the booster snack they will use in the race. This not only prepares the stomach for the race, the boost will

Avoid the following:

Salt—Salt consumed during the 24 hours before the race will produce blood more concentrated in sodium. Fluid is then taken from muscle tissue and other areas, reducing your capacity for performance through dehydration.

Fat—The more fat in your diet the day before a long one (especially after 2 p.m.), the more sluggish your digestive system and the less effective the food will be in delivering nutrients that can be used during the race. Because it takes a longer time to process, a fatty meal often causes stomach or bowel problems the next day. Fat is not a good thing...in the long one.

Fiber—Too much loading up on fiber foods the day before the long one (or race morning) can lead to unloading. Not only is this embarrassing, it's dehydrating.

Large meals the night before the long training sessions or races will still be in your intestines, drawing blood away from the exercising muscles the next morning.

Alcohol—This central nervous system depressant will leave you with less motivation the next morning. This will interfere with your goal, whether it be for a time or to finish. Alcohol is also a major dehydrating agent.

help you get through the speed session and recover faster.

CAFFEINE

If you are used to drinking a cup of coffee before exercise, there's no reason why you shouldn't have a cup before a long run or a race (see the last section of the previous chapter). Only about half of the fluid in the cup of coffee will be available for use by the body so don't account for the whole cup in your hydration computation. Caffeine is a central nervous system stimulant that helps to get your mind and body up to speed from the beginning of a workout. It promotes an early breakdown of body fat and has been shown to increase endurance capacity. And, yes, it can get one important personal detail taken care of early so that you don't have to spend time in the portajohn before the race (or wish you could).

Galloway's picks:

LOWFAT FOODS THAT INCREASE SATISFACTION*

Protein:
Nonfat or lowfat chicken breasts (frozen)

Nonfat or lowfat deli turkey

Egg whites

Soy burgers

Some white fish (many fish have a high fat content)

Vegetables
Most cooked vegetables

Salads

Cole slaw with nonfat mayonnaise

Soup—in cans or dry mix in a cup

Filler foods
Baked potatoes

Brown rice (feel satisfied longer)

White rice

Cereal
Grape Nuts can be added to many snacks to prolong satisfaction

Oatmeal with fruit or in a smoothie

Oat bran can be added to drinks, soup, pancakes, muffins and bread

Fruits
Smoothies with oat bran

Baked goods
Whole grain or crusty and fibrous bread

Small meals
Oat bran pancakes or waffles with smoothie topping (bananas, strawberries and orange juice)

Grape Nuts, banana, grapes or sliced apples

Whole grain or oat bran bagel with lowfat or fatfree cream cheese

Baked potato (skin and all), fatfree cream cheese, low or nonfat cole slaw

Turkey breast or ground turkey burgers with vegetable of choice

Chicken breast with rice, vegetables, whole grain breads

Smoothie: any fruit (1-3 varieties) and fruit juice

Example: banana, frozen strawberries, OJ concentrate, yogurt, oat bran (if desired)

Energy bars

*remember to drink water with every snack

The reloading zone

The best window for reloading after exercise is within 30 minutes of finishing your workout. But you can still get some reloading benefits for the next two hours. Be sure to drink water or other fluids (except for those with caffeine and alcohol) during the reloading process. By drinking fluid and eating some quality carbohydrate snack (enhanced by adding about 20 percent protein by calorie count), you can maximize glycogen reloading and therefore feel better and stronger during your next workout.

Vitamins and Minerals

I'm not a proponent of filling up your shelves with pills. A variety of fresh fruits and vegetables with lean protein will usually give you more of the nutrients that you need. If you suspect that your diet is not delivering, take a "one a day" type vitamin, such as Cooper Complete. Some good research points to the possibility of cancer reduction if you take Vitamin C (500mg) and Vitamin E (400iu) every day. Vitamin C definitely speeds up the healing process. Women who exercise regularly tend to be low in iron and sometimes calcium. *For more information, visit www. JeffGalloway.com.*

Alcohol

This central nervous system depressant is almost certain to lower your performance if consumed within about 12 hours of exercise. The more you drink, the longer the depressing effect lasts. Alcohol dehydrates you also. It's not a good idea to drink the night before a significant workout (long, fast or a race).

Caffeine

Caffeine is a central nervous system stimulant that can enhance exercise performance and enjoyment. But there are a few individuals who shouldn't partake. Those who have irregular heartbeat problems, for example, shouldn't be drinking coffee. If you suspect that you are one of these few people, check with your doctor or a sports nutritionist.

You will lose about half the water in a cup of coffee or diet cola. This means that half of the fluid is available for absorption. It is still wise to moderate your use of caffeine products. A cup of coffee before a race is fine if you're accustomed to doing this before exercise. It's not a great idea, however, to drink three or more cups or diet drinks before going to the starting line.

I dearly enjoy my cup of coffee before my workouts. It not only raises my awareness, concentration and motivation, but it seems to get the right brain working its intuitive magic and cranking out creative thoughts.

Research shows that caffeine stimulates an early breakdown of your body fat into substances that can be burned as fuel, free fatty acids and triglycerides. There's also good evidence that drinking a cup of coffee about an hour before exercise improves your endurance.

I just feel better on a run after a cup of coffee...or two.

64

Long term nutritional health

I recommend that you do additional reading in sports nutrition and gradually mod-
ify your diet. After reading through five
or 10 good resource books on nutrition,
you'll see that the principles in agreement
are the following:

- It's important to reduce dietary fat over
  time, including trans fat.

- It's best to get your nutrients mostly in
  food.

- A variety of foods, including fresh fruit
  and vegetables, will deliver nutrients
  well.

- It's better to eat seven to nine smaller
  meals a day rather than two to three
  bigger ones.

- In each meal, try to balance mostly
  complex carbohydrates with some
  protein and a little fat.

- Most women and some men tend to
  be low in iron and should supplement.

- Supplementing vitamins E and C may
  help in preventing certain types of
  cancer.

- In changing your diet, do it over three
  to five years, five being better than
  three.

The percentages vary as do the programs
to deliver nutrients. You will find the com-
binations that work best for you.

65

MOTIVATION

THE SOURCE OF MOTIVATION

Just a few minutes each day will keep you motivated and will make you a more positive person.

*T*here are many quick fixes which can get you out the door or a mile down the road. I actually like to have, as a last resort, some of these "dirty tricks" (which will be noted in a later chapter) ready when the primary motivation elements are not working. But it's actually quite easy to stay motivated by expressing the positive thoughts, feelings and momentum you receive from your exercise. Just a few minutes each day will help you understand the process of staying motivated and will make you a more positive person. In this section you'll find a range of concepts and techniques which have helped thousands of exercisers find the spark inside to meet any challenge, starting with rolling out of bed when the alarm goes off.

Following are a series of tips for getting motivated staying motivated, and breaking through barriers. Throughout, you'll discover successful strategies for maximizing use of the creative and intuitive right side of the brain. Once you realize how to keep the left side under control, you'll be able to do what you're capable of doing. All of us have much more potential than we usually allow ourselves to explore. It is my mission in the following chapters to help you tap into those strength areas inside you so that you can head toward the accomplishment you

desire—including getting more enjoyment out of life.

Yes, you can train yourself to be motivated, stay motivated and, then, in the next section, break through barriers. The same principle applies: regularity of practice doing exercises which realistically simulate the problems you will face. But before we talk about the exercises, let's look at the bigger picture and, at the same time, find ways to have more fun as we exercise.

THE LEFT SIDE OF OUR BRAIN TRIES TO HOLD US BACK

Inside the left hemisphere at the top of your head is the center of logic. The left brain solves math problems, organizes and nitpicks, and conducts the structured cognitive activities during your workday. One of the primary missions of the left brain is to steer you in the direction of pleasure and away from discomfort. Any form of stress or perceived stress will stimulate this negative center of logic to produce a stream of messages to "slow down!" or "quit!" or to question your sanity: "Why are you doing this?"

Because we rely upon the left side for logical guidance, we listen to these messages. If we're weak or tired, we're very likely to give in to the messages and compromise our goal. Certainly we must always monitor the real dangers which could produce health problems (heat buildup, traffic, overfatigue) and take action when there is due cause. Most of the time, however, our left brain overreacts in warning us long before we are in real danger. Motivation training desensitizes us to the extraneous negative messages and the left brain's nagging style. You can also set up a positive mental response to the negative left side that will reduce its effect and allow you to head toward your goal at a speed that is within your capabilities.

THE RIGHT BRAIN

Your creative and intuitive center is in the right side of your brain. Running and walking are two of the best ways to tap into this resource, as long as you're going slowly enough to stay within your capabilities. This right side is a reservoir of creative solutions to just about any problem, challenge or obstacle. Through pacing, walk/shuffle breaks and blood sugar-boosting, you can cut down dramatically on stress, reducing the negative left brain messages so that you stay on the right (brain) track. Later in this section, I'll go over some proven methods of stimulating right brain activity. To maximize time in the wonderful world of the right brain, become sensitive to the stress buildup of your workouts and the race itself. Only you have the complete power to reduce the intensity and disconnect the negative speaker of the left brain before it makes your exercise seem like work.

FUN

Before we go any further we must bring in the magic ingredient which keeps you motivated under just about any situation. When you find ways to have fun during exercise, you open the door for the right brain to take over and work its creative magic. You may

begin it by reading a funny story before the start or visiting a coffee shop with interesting characters. It also helps to run with a person or group or exercise on a favorite trail... Don't stop with my suggestions. The best ones are those that allow you to enjoy parts of a workout or the whole thing. Anything that makes your training session special and interesting to you should be included in your bag of fun tricks.

VISION AND FOCUS

No one stays totally motivated all of the time. Those who are more successful sometimes seem to be always fired up, but they have down times like everyone else. By concentrating on the positive aspects of your exercise, several times a day, you become focused on something that makes you feel good. It only takes a few seconds every two hours or so and you'll be motivated to get out there and collect your endorphins.

THE VISION EXERCISE

You only need to spend a few relaxed moments each day to collect your positive thoughts about exercise and what makes you feel confident, looking forward to the next workout. Do a quick reality check with your vision to see how your present position relates to the larger vision you have for the next six to 12 months. Those who don't spend these few moments to stay focused often are guided by dreams and illusions which lead in one direction and then, in no direction at all.

THE DIFFERENCE BETWEEN A DREAM AND A VISION

A dream is not connected to reality. It's easy to dream that you'll run below two hours in the marathon. Yes, you can dream far beyond your capabilities and set yourself up for great disappointment. At the instant of your dream, you may be exhilarated. But

"I'm looking forward to my run"

- The physical exertion will feel good.

- My legs want to go.

- The increased blood circulation makes me feel more alive.

- I love the way I feel afterward: relaxed and focused, with a great attitude.

- My family appreciates the way I am after exercise.

- It's so great to work out in the morning, getting the mind and spirit mobilized and focused for the day.

- My afternoon run/walk takes away the stress, getting me ready to enjoy my family.

- During the second half of my workout and afterward, I'm in another world, swimming in endorphins.

without a plan and the reality checks along the way, motivation is lost very quickly. Even when dreams are within your capabilities, without a well-structured training program and regular mental contact with your vision, dreams are seldom realized. In contrast, a vision is a series of images that can be molded over several months into a realistic behavioral plan that is put into action every week. In effect, you're a sculptor who molds an elusive image into a series of real experiences that have all of the elements that prepare you for and lead you to a goal that is realistic, fulfilling and engaging.

A vision is a realistic future behavioral experience that you can prepare for by specific physical and mental exercises. To truly fulfill a vision, you must chart out these exercises, constantly adjusting and fine-tuning them to make the vision more complete and meaningful to you. Then, you end up with a final product that is much better than the one you started with. With each adjustment, you get more involved in the process and become more motivated.

TRANSFORMING THE VISION INTO A MISSION SUSTAINS MOTIVATION

Adding the behavioral elements to your vision starts with the writing of the date of your specific goal event (marathon, half marathon, etc.) on a calendar. Actually, the process often starts weeks or months before. It may be the snapshot of an overweight friend finishing a marathon. "If Suzi can do it, I can too," you say. You enter a half marathon and write the date on your kitchen calendar. The mission begins with your first run/walk, a three-miler. During each long one you will solve new problems, make adjustments and apply the revised vision to the mental rehearsal of the next long one. All the way through the program, you're making your vision more realistic as you stay on track all the way to the finish, wearing a big smile.

IT STARTS WITH A DATE ON THE CALENDAR

A significant mission, such as a half or full marathon, will get your attention and motivate you to do things you haven't done in years. Instead of rolling over, you'll get out of bed an hour early and cover the miles, feeling better for it. After those "bad days" at work, you'll find a way to get on the roads because you have that race scribbled

69

on your kitchen calendar. You're rewarded by an erasure of most of the stress of the day. There's something powerful about the act of giving yourself a deadline that pushes you down the road on days when you'd just as soon cut the run short.

REGULARITY IS IMPORTANT

While it is possible to miss several workouts and still survive the race, most exercisers who try this drop out of the program. The longer you wait to return to exercise, the more negative messages you receive, which can keep you from getting out there. If this is your problem, put "regularity" at the top of your list of commitments. *Hint: On the "bad" days, just get out for 10 minutes.*

AN EXTENDED FOCUS

As you notice changes in yourself, you extend the positive effects into other areas of life. You have a better attitude at home, enjoying the time with your spouse and the kids much more. Stress doesn't bother you as it did before. You can deal with problems more directly, and you maintain focus to the finish of your work projects. Everything in your life can be better when you exercise regularly.

GETTING MOTIVATED:
THE INSPIRATION MUSCLE IS THE HARDEST TO FLEX

Inside of each of us is all the motivation we need to get going and stay motivated.

After six to 12 months of regular exercise, most goal-oriented exercisers have made the lifestyle adjustments which make exercise a scheduled and important part of the day. Before we get to that point, it's necessary to make an effort to reinforce the regularity of exercise and maintain the daily run or walk as a top priority. Sometimes it's as simple as learning to appreciate the rewards, such as relaxing endorphins. You've been receiving them all along, but you didn't take time to enjoy.

But everyone will have to find some extra insertions of fun from time to time. Some exercisers look for different birds or flowers during a workout. Others test the winter weather and look forward to the challenge of layering to meet the colder temperatures. A dip in the pool or a mid-workout shower can get you out the door and keep you out there when the thermometer tops the 85° mark.

Most of those who say they just need a little motivation to get into shape are only dreaming. Yes, they have a dream of being a stronger, firmer, more active person, but the dream is not attached to the behaviors which bring it into reality. Dreams are the illusive things that go through your head at

Affirming the benefits of exercise

When you're tentative about your motivation to get out the door, it often helps to read (possibly out loud) the following list of benefits you receive afterward:

- Your attitude is better.
- Stress is released, often completely dissolved.
- Natural body chemicals called endorphins relax the body, reducing or eliminating muscle aches and pains.
- Your spirit is engaged, leaving you with feelings of accomplishment, confidence and strength.
- Body and mind are connected, giving you the confidence that comes with being a more "complete" person.
- Your right brain is engaged, energizing your creative and imaginative resources.
- You're learning connections to hidden inner resources which kick in whenever you're under stress.

For more reasons, see Getting Started, www.jeffgalloway.com.

71

night. An image without a series of weekly workouts will stay, merely, an image. If you really want to change behaviors, believing that you can is only the first step. It is the behavioral vision of moving the legs every other day which can change body shape and improve mental outlook. An idea or image is powerful only if it is practiced, refined and then changed into a vision of permanent lifestyle where exercise is fun.

CONFIDENCE IN THE PROGRAM

To get motivated, exercisers at all levels need to feel that each day's workout and the program as a whole is doable. When in doubt, it's always better to err on the side of a less demanding program or one that has flexibility. It also helps to study the program before beginning to determine your level of confidence in the schedule and the designer before you get in over your head.

BE PREPARED TO BACK UP

72

Practically everyone who trains for a half or full marathon has setbacks. You're going to be more motivated to stay on a program if you know that it's possible to add more walk or shuffle breaks, for example, or reschedule the long ones. Since there's a wide range of abilities and fitness backgrounds, individuals will progress at different rates, and some schedules don't allow for this.

THE RIGHT GROUP WILL MOTIVATE YOU

If you can find a group of goal-oriented exercisers at your ability level in your area, join it. Because the group is waiting for you, you'll roll out of bed on mornings you wouldn't otherwise. The chemistry, fun and bonding that comes from the group will have you looking forward to the next one. You'll get as much out of helping others as being pulled along on your "dog days."

Choose a group that...

Is composed of people at your level—not the level you want to achieve

Takes walk/shuffle breaks from the beginning of all long ones

Goes at a pace that allows you to finish long ones without breathing so hard that you can't carry on a conversation

Gives you a feeling of comfort and acceptance

Meets at a time and place which would fit into your lifestyle

Visit www.JeffGalloway.com "Training Programs."

WHAT IF THERE ARE NO GROUPS IN YOUR AREA

If you're having trouble getting out for a workout, put on your running shoes and clothes and call a friend who will talk you out the door. There are a growing number of online running companions for the same reasons. *(For more info on groups in your area, see the Galloway Training Program page in the back of this book. Jeff Galloway and others offer Ecoaching.)*

IT COULD BE LOW BLOOD SUGAR

You may be just half an energy bar away from motivation. If your exercise time is midday or later and you feel tired and unmotivated, you may suffer from low blood sugar. Waiting for more than two hours to eat a balanced snack or meal (high sugar foods make the situation worse) will lower your concentration and motivation. Low blood sugar is a significant stress on your system, causing the left side of your brain to

When I have a cup of coffee and an energy bar, I feel that I can do anything!

unleash a stream of messages, such as the following: "You'll feel better tomorrow, take the day off," "You have too much to do," or "You'll feel so much better on the couch." An energy snack, with water, about one hour before exercise, will often turn off the negative and get you off the couch.

MISSION: GETTING OUT THE DOOR AFTER A HARD DAY AT WORK

Even the most dedicated exerciser has days when the gravity that pulls one back to the bed or couch is much stronger than usual. Anyone can become successful at starting a walk or run by setting up a process similar to getting a model train moving when it is just short of the top of a hill. A few extra pushes or pulls to get the momentum started and you're moving down the road with that same momentum. Those who are successful in getting regularly out the door spend a little time at the beginning to set up a process with a reward system. After going through the series of steps that gets you going, over and over again, one step will lead automatically to the next one.

ONE TINY STEP AFTER ANOTHER... OUT THE DOOR

Let's say that it was a bad day at work and you really don't want to exercise. Your mission, should you choose to accept it, is to get the body in motion using whatever tricks, rewards, etc. are necessary. Here's a simple "script" that has helped thousands of folks get moving—and stay moving until the endorphins start flowing. You'll need to adapt the following to your situation and rehearse it over and over, especially on your way home after work each day. The more

Whatever your challenge, the "scripted" approach has three components:

1. Lowering your anticipated discomfort—and telling the left brain to take it easy

2. Setting up a series of small steps, no one of which is difficult enough to produce stress or alert left brain radar

3. Rehearsing through the sequence of small steps so many times that you move from one to the next almost automatically

you rehearse it, even on days when you don't need the motivation, the more likely you will move from one step to the next when you hit a low.

Scene # 1: You're driving home after a terrible work day, hungry, and your left brain has a dozen reasons why you shouldn't exercise.

Action:

1. Lie to the left brain, saying "I'm not going to exercise today. I'll take it easy around the house in some comfortable clothes."

2. You arrive home and immediately put on running shoes and clothes telling yourself, "I'm not going to exercise today, just going to be comfortable around here."

73

> **The crossing of a street usually breaks the bond of the couch and signals that you're on your way!**

3. Eat a energy bar or other energy snack and drink your beverage of choice (hint: caffeine helps if you're okay with it).

4. Put on some inspirational music and read some of the affirmations in this chapter and the last one.

5. Stick your head out the door to see what the weather is doing and then just step outside.

6. Walk to the edge of the block to see what the neighbors are doing.

7. Cross the street and you're on your way!

Scene # 2: From the bed to the street

74 **Action:**

Here's another challenge for many exercisers: getting out of bed early enough to do the morning workout. Again, you should individualize this to your own needs and situation.

1. Look at your clock the night before. Tell yourself what time you will be getting up. Go through a quick mental rehearsal of yourself hearing the alarm and getting out of bed. Have your clothes laid out so that you can put them on without thinking.

2. The alarm goes off. Without thinking, your feet go on the floor.

3. Without thinking, stand up and head for the kitchen.

4. Prepare your beverage of choice: coffee, tea, juice, smoothie, etc.

5. Sip your beverage and put on clothes as automatically as possible.

6. Walk out the door, not thinking about going any distance at all.

7. Walk to the street to see what the neighbors are doing.

8. Cross the street and you're on your way!

STAYING MOTIVATED

***A** body on the couch wants to stay there. But once a body is in motion, it wants to continue in motion.*

*J*ust as any motivated exerciser will have low motivation to start some days, everyone reaches plateaus. This chapter is dedicated to helping you continue individual workouts when you want to stop. Also included are some of my secrets for staying on a schedule when you hit the natural motivation lulls.

FORWARD MOTION EXERCISE IS MOTIVATING IN ITSELF

If you start your workout slowly enough, it only takes a minute or two to be rewarded by the flow of relaxing endorphins and attitude enhancing mental hormones. You may need to walk very often, but moving forward is naturally pleasurable to the body and mind when done at an easy pace.

GET A MISSION AND WRITE IT ON THE CALENDAR

When you pick a challenge like a half or full marathon and write the date on your calendar, you're more likely to be motivated on those hot, muggy days or when looking at snowflakes falling. Everyone knows that an event as long as, say, 13.1 or 26.2 miles, requires preparation. This pulls you out of bed when the temperature outside is in the 90's or 10° below, and it keeps you going when you get the urge to cut the workout short.

A MID-WORKOUT MOTIVATION CRISIS IS ALMOST ALWAYS THE RESULT OF GOING TOO FAST, FOR YOU, ON THAT DAY

The more stress you place on yourself, the more negative messages you'll receive from the left brain, which will lead to a desire to quit. Ease up, take more walk or shuffle breaks, and you'll get through most of these "walls." If the weather presents you with too much heat/humidity and/or you went too fast in the beginning or the middle, it may be too late to do anything but walk slowly. Learn from this, and back off early the next time.

BRING AN ENERGY GEL WITH YOU

Your preferred blood sugar food can pull you out of motivational lulls. Everyone will experience a blood sugar crash at some distance. By consuming products like energy gels or energy bars (with water), almost all exercisers will be able to keep blood sugar (and motivation) at a high level. These products also help on short sessions if you haven't eaten enough prior to the start.

BE SURE THAT YOU'RE NOT HAVING A MEDICAL PROBLEM

It's extremely rare, but there are a few times when you should not push through barriers. If you have or suspect a medical emergency—stress fracture, cardiovascular problem, heat disease, etc., stop immediately and get help. In fact, this is approximately a million-to-one occurrence. Even though this is a very unlikely event, it's always better to be safe than sorry. If there are good reasons why your ache or pain can lead to significant health risks, it's always better to quit early and talk to a doctor.

A second level of medical alert relates to overtraining and injury. Some aches and pains are early warning signs of injuries or excessive fatigue. Experienced exercisers become very sensitive to the weak links: those knees, tendons, muscles that become injured most often. By backing off early or taking an extra day off, you may avoid weeks or months of layoff later—because you tried to push through an early-stage injury.

ON THE VERY TOUGH OR FAST ONES

Almost every exerciser has at least one tough workout every month. Whether it occurs during a tour around the block or during a 23-miler or speed session, here are my tricks for continuing:

1. Slow down and allow the body and mind to get a break. Take more walk or shuffle breaks as needed, take more rest between intervals in a speed session, and start back into the workout slower than before. The earlier you make an adjustment, the better quality you'll be able to salvage from that workout.

2. Break up the remaining distance into segments that you know you can do. Take a walk break (or a shuffle break) every 1 to 3 minutes. You know that you can go another minute, right? If 1 minute is too long, try 30 seconds. Your workout is a series of these segments to the finish line.

3. Use distractions. Look ahead to the next mailbox, stop sign, fast food restaurant, water stop, etc., and tell yourself that you can take a break there. Make sure the segment is short enough so that you feel confident in getting there.

4. Focus on the person ahead of the person in front of you. By looking ahead, you can be pulled past the person in front of you if you're in a group or a race. Stay mentally attached to that person, noting the outfit, the printing, the hat, etc. If you're only looking at details, you'll at least be preoccupying the left brain so that it won't zing you as badly or as often. See the section on "dirty tricks" you can play on the left brain.

5. Use a mantra. There are various types of words and phrases which will do more than distract you. Practice these and develop your own to put yourself into a positive trance. See the sidebar on the next page for more suggestions.

6. Don't give up. If you respond to each thought of quitting with the internal resolve that you are going to finish, you will! Positive mental attitude alone can pull you through many difficult situations.

76

Mantras for Staying Motivated (to be said over and over)

Strength mantras will connect into your hidden resources that keep you going when tired. The specific words you choose will help to make subconscious and intuitive connections with muscles and your inner resolve. As you learn to tap into the right brain, you'll coin phrases that continue drawing on mental or spiritual resources. The following have been used when under physical and mental stress, but use these only as a primer. The best ones will be your own mantras that relate to your experiences with words that work. Action phrases not only keep you going but also help you perform as you find ways to dig deeper into your resources.

Feet—stay light and quick, keep moving

My legs are strong

My heart is pumping better

More blood in the muscles

Lactic acid, go away

More oxygen, lungs

The strength is in there, I'm feeling it

Talk crazy to me, right brain

I'm feeling creative—I'm making adjustments

I feel comfortable—I'm in control

I feel good—I feel strong

I'm floating

Come to me—endorphins

I'm having fun

Distraction Mantras start by preoccupying your left brain so that it won't send you so many negative messages. After saying these over many times, you may be able to shift into the right brain.

Look at that store, car, building, sign, etc.

Look at that person, hair, outfit, hat, T-shirt design, etc.

One more step, one more step

One more block, telephone pole, stop light, etc.

Baby steps, baby steps, baby steps

Vision Mantras help you feel that you're getting where you want to be.

I can see the next mile marker

I can feel the pull of the finish line

I can feel being pulled along by the runners ahead

I can feel myself getting stronger

I'm pushing through the wall

I'm moving at the right pace to finish with strength

Funny Mantras get you to laugh, which is a right brain activity.

I feel like a clown, ballerina, football player, stooge

Float like an anchor, sting like a sponge

Where's the bounce, glide

Creative Mantras

I'm building a house, railroad, community, bookcase, etc.

What type of novel could that person ahead of me have written?

What type of crime could that person on the sidewalk be plotting?

What type of movie could be staged here?

77

IF YOUR GOAL ISN'T MOTIVATING ANY MORE

Having gone through more than 130 marathon training programs, I've experienced many motivation letdowns. On most of these, I've rebounded, but on a few, I didn't. Burnout and dropout are mental injuries. If you back off and adjust early, you can avoid major burnout later.

Getting Beyond the Mid-Goal Wall

1. Reduce mileage and cut your workout days to three. Put a lot of easy walking into those.

2. Run or walk in scenic areas, places that really motivate you.

3. Schedule a social run with a friend or a group of friends. Tell him, her or them that you need help. Have a good time and meet afterward for a snack or meal.

4. Do anything necessary to add more fun to your program: after-workout rewards, special outfits or shoes after specific long ones, etc.

5. Adjust your goal event so that it is more motivating. Stay at a special hotel, get some friends to meet you there, or schedule weekend activities with your family (at events such as the Breast Cancer Marathon).

6. Sometimes it helps to choose another goal event and adjust your training accordingly.

BREAKING THROUGH BARRIERS

STAYING FOCUSED ON THE BIG DAY

A MENTAL TOUR
OF THE EVENT

A thorough mental rehearsal of one of life's challenges will mobilize all of your resources and bring mind and body together.

*B*efore attempting something challenging like a half or full marathon, wouldn't you love to have the confidence of having done it—without the fatigue, sweat, aches and pains? Thanks to the wonderful world of visualization, this is now possible. So lace up your mental shoes, and let's start reducing the effect of the negative left brain messages.

In this chapter, we're going to rehearse the event so that you can overcome the challenge in the experience. The better your rehearsal, the more prepared you'll be for the race itself. Draw upon your experience from the long ones to construct your mental event. The more challenges you rehearse, the less effect they will have should you encounter them in the race itself.

REHEARSE!

We're going to take a mental tour of the event. By doing this over and over again, you'll develop a confidence in finishing which is similar to that of veteran racers. Even more significantly, you'll be gradually adding realistic details and situations to positively overcome the physical and mental challenge experiences. This mental *conditioning* will make you tougher and will build the specific confidence needed to confront

Rehearsal Benefits

Fast forward Mentally rehearsing the race gears up mind and body for the sequence of events. The more times you're able to rehearse, the more smoothly you'll mentally prepare for each segment of the event and the better you'll anticipate your need for resources and adjusting for success.

Left brain garbage The negative messages released under stress are reduced because you've desensitized yourself to them. In other words, there's less stress, therefore less garbage.

Mind-body teamwork develops better in mental rehearsals because you can edit and improve responses in a short period of mental rehearsal time. This doesn't get you out of doing your long ones, of course. Once you've had two to three runs over 15 miles, you have an experience base that will allow you to convert 15 minutes of mental rehearsal time into months of training experience.

You gain control! Instead of waiting for things to happen or taking what comes your way, rehearsal allows you to set up the steps you'll take to get through each stage and challenge of the race.

the same problems in the race itself. Your long ones help you to 'desensitize' to most or all of the possible items which *could* go wrong. You can then anticipate and find solutions or inner strength to get the job done.

Probably the greatest benefit you'll receive from rehearsal is the opportunity to mold your experience in advance, setting up a blueprint for the challenge of the race. At the same time, you gain insight into the series of possible challenges facing you. Each long one will teach you a few more lessons as it tosses up problems to solve. By the time you've done your longest one, all of the major challenges will have been encountered (except for changes in weather). As you rehearse yourself through each successive long one, make the adjustments which you didn't make the last time. The process gets easier and easier even though you're dealing with a greater number of rough edges, components and anxieties.

The object is not to solve every problem. Many of the doubts, anxieties, aches and pains just go away as you make a few minor adjustments, dig down a little deeper and keep going. By setting up every possible problem you could have in your rehearsal, you'll start the right brain looking for solutions.

As you're being realistic, unleash your creativity. Include in your rehearsal a few unexpected situations that you haven't faced yet. This will reduce your shock and stress if and when these occur in the race itself. Be sure to insert some fun rehearsal elements, such as strange people along the way, interesting conversations with your fellow travelers, and landmarks. I want you to enjoy your race, and mental rehearsal will increase the likelihood of this.

PRINCIPLES OF MENTAL REHEARSAL

- Break down the experience into a series of small events:

1. None of which is challenging in itself

2. Each of which leads directly and automatically to the next

- Desensitize yourself to the uncomfortable parts:

1. By mentally experiencing them, they aren't as bad when you run into them.

2. The more you rehearse problems, the more solutions you may find for them.

3. When you mentally "tough it out" in rehearsal, over and over, it's easier to "gut it out" in the race itself.

- Rehearse every possible "problem" you could have in the race - talk to veterans:

1. When in doubt, rehearse it—it's better to be prepared for anything.

2. Rehearse each situation to be worse than you expect it to be in the race.

   · Problems which are less intense than rehearsed are less likely to engage the negative left side of the brain.

- Rehearse often!

1. Rehearse parts of the race every day.

2. Concentrate on those aspects which make you the most apprehensive.

3. Go through each segment, dealing with each problem and getting through it.

4. Mentally, you can find several solutions to the same problem.

5. At least once a week, do at least a quick mental rehearsal of the race, as we are doing now.

THE MENTAL RACE...STEP BY STEP

First, let's talk through the night before. You've had a full day of walking around the expo,

- drinking 6 to 8 ounces of water each hour or two,

- snacking on energy bars and other low-fat (low-salt) snacks all day and all evening, and

- sharing good experiences with friends and with other exercisers from around the country.

Now that it's bedtime...what's going through your mind?

"I'm not going to sleep a wink."

"It's going to be rough tomorrow."

"What have I gotten myself into?"

Yes, all of these are legitimate messages which will come...and pass through. These negative thoughts will leak out of your left brain, which is programmed to respond to stress. The more you frame the race as a stressful experience, the more negative messages you'll receive. But it's just as easy to frame it as a positively challenging journey.

THE BATTLE: LEFT BRAIN VS RIGHT BRAIN

- An inner-brain conflict will occur every time you put yourself to the challenge.

- The left side has a million logical reasons why you can't do something.

- The right side won't try to argue; it will just try to get the job done using its unlimited supply of creative, spontane-

ous and imaginative ways of steering you in the direction of that which you are capable.

- In most cases, it's easy to get out of left brain control by relaxing, taking the pressure off yourself, and engaging in a right brain activity, such as laughing, story-telling, or low-level physical activity (walking, for example).

Okay, now, how about some positive thoughts about the race?

"Knowing it's over"

"Having my psychiatrist tell me that I'm okay—even if I want to do a half or full marathon"

"The satisfaction of finishing with the medal around my neck"

On the first two, your left brain is still in control. Now the medal...the medal around the neck...That's the bottom line! Let's start there—you're wearing your medal! Sure, there are aches and pains, but overpowering it all is the feeling of accomplishment and personal satisfaction. This is a significant achievement which you did with your own resources. You had to pull from the various sources of your inner strengths and you did. No one can ever take this achievement away.

This glow will color every other part of the experience. When you start to feel unequal to the task, you'll come back to this very powerful inner feeling which you receive from finishing.

THE NIGHT BEFORE

Yes, you're nervous, but it's normal to feel this way. You've got everything laid out for the morning according to your checklist.

When the Left Brain Bothers You.....

*Diffuse the stress by saying that you're **not** going to push yourself:*

- It's going to be a walk (or very slow jog).
- You have all the time in the world to finish.
- This is your day to smell the roses.

Focus on the positive effect of your race experience:

- You feel more invigorated.
- The training has improved your attitude.
- Your focus is better.
- You're positive because you're doing something very positive for yourself.

Gain a vision of yourself crossing the finish line:

- Sure you're tired but you're excited and fulfilled.
- The sense of accomplishment is unlike anything you've ever experienced.
- You've found new sources of strength inside.
- The medal around your neck symbolizes all of this—bestows a wonderful glow.

Walk around or jog around:

- The forward motion creates positive momentum.

- Your body is designed for forward motion and responds positively when you move.
- Natural endorphins relax you and settle you down.
- This gets the right brain connected to the body, allowing you to bypass the left brain.

Tell a joke:

- Laughing helps to engage the right brain.
- It bestows a gutteral confidence.
- Collect a few funny thoughts and jokes which you can call up with a key word.
- Even if you tell it to yourself, learn how to laugh with yourself.

Have a number of positive success stories:

- The best ones are the many little successes you've had in the training.
- You can also draw from the success stories of others.
- Trade stories with the others around you.
- Positive behavioral experiences build a positive attitude and inspire positive behavior.

You may be so nervous that you won't sleep at all. That's also okay because you don't need to sleep the night before a race. The crucial nights are the two before the last one. Sleep deprivation may be a good thing when it's limited to the night before the race. Many marathoners, including some world-class performers, have run their best times after a sleepless night. The important concept is that lack of sleep is not going to bother you. In other words, it's not the lack of sleep, it's the worrying about not sleeping the night before which will engage the left brain and produce negative messages.

So you're resting, thinking about all of the things that are about to happen to you. You may decide to read or you may just lie there resting. If it's an out of town event, be sure to bring a magazine, book or something which can keep your interest in those hours of quiet. Positive, interesting concepts or stories are best, but anything that has worked in the past is fine. I bring along the newspapers which pile up on my doorstep between trips.

WAKE-UP CALL

You're motivated to get going and begin a water-drinking routine: four to six ounces every half hour. As you collect the items on your checklist (see Practical Advice), you develop a vision of the positive, successful feeling you're going to have with the medal around your neck. When the negative side of your brain, the left side, starts to send negative messages, think of the medal around your neck and move into some productive activity.

THE LINE UP

Hopefully, you'll be connecting with friends as you go to the start. It helps to know, in advance, about the area of the start, how you'll get there, the problems, etc. In New York City, for example, you must board a bus quite early and sit under a tent for several hours. At the Marine Corps Marathon, you will be walking or taking the Metro to the start, in all probability, and it's a fairly long walk.

You're joking with friends or folks as you walk to your starting position and wait for the gun. You've spent a little time preparing for this with some interesting stories and jokes, which you will be sharing. As you're laughing, you realize that the left brain is kept under control and can't unload many negative thoughts.

It's natural to feel nervous and to be excited. Settle yourself down by saying things such as "I feel relaxed and ready to glide" and "I've prepared and have plenty of power." When you receive even the hint of a left brain message (and you will), squelch it with a positive behavioral thought, such as the vision of yourself going across the finish line. Take a few steps as you mentally rehearse those good thoughts.

THE START

You begin to get uneasy when the announcer calls everyone to the start. But as you share energy with the people around you, tell jokes, or mentally revisit some very successful experiences, you're feeling comfortable and secure. The gun fires and you gently move with the people around you. You're all in this together, moving forward towards a positive goal. It's a mass migration in which you're destined to triumph!

At times, you'll be tempted to go faster to express a few hidden, competitive urges (which you may not know you have). But you hold back. Realizing that there is plenty of time and distance to go at the pace you wish, the first few congested miles don't bother you as you continue to go with the flow. Several times you find yourself feeling good and starting to go faster than you know you're ready to do so you return to a realistic pace (or better, a conservative one).

You're tempted to not take the first few shuffle or walk breaks, pushed forward by your left brain ego. But at each place for a walk/shuffle break, you do it. As people go by, and you're tempted to cut the break short, you resist the temptation. Soon you're into the flow of the breaks—mentally segmenting the distance.

If the left brain tries to insert a stress message about how far you have left to the finish, you immediately focus on your next break, saying out loud 'just ___ more minutes' (fill in the number of minutes/seconds you'll run before walking - or walk before shuffling).

After a few miles you'll make it a game to focus on a few individuals who are going at your desired pace. You follow them with your eyes as they get ahead on walk/shuffle breaks, and you playfully catch up with them by the end of each run or walk segment. During the second half, you'll have to choose another set of people because your original group has dropped off the pace because they didn't take the breaks.

CHALLENGES

It is better to know the course you will be using (see the specific course descriptions in the race flyers or on the websites). But if you're unsure of exactly which course you'll be using, you can rehearse a generic race. It's even better to over-rehearse the challenges; if you're prepared for a more difficult experience, then a less demanding one won't engage the left brain as much.

Hills present a variety of challenges. In the early stages, you may have a tendency to run or walk a bit too hard going up so you hold yourself back. When you reach a difficult uphill, a slight shortening of the stride will relax the legs again and keep you moving with strength. When hills get difficult later on, you continue to shorten the stride, even as short as tiny 'baby steps,' if needed. This allows you to keep moving and get the job done. It's always better to rehearse hills that are longer, steeper and more frequent than those actually on the course. If you over-rehearse the difficulty of the last six miles of the race, you'll be in a better position to enjoy the end of the race itself.

The most significant challenges will come during the last three to six miles when the

left brain is going to be activitated by a variety of stresses: blisters, aches, fatigue, low blood sugar, dehydration. Your greatest enemy at any point in the race comes not from the stress or even the negative left brain messages which are generated by them: it's the internal doubt which your left brain promotes and upon which it feeds. By focusing on magic words and phrases which feature your past successes, you'll have a great tendency to ignore the alarmist negativism and earn your success.

GUTTING IT OUT

Most of the problems, insecurities and resulting negative messages can be managed and overcome by digging down a little deeper into your reservoir of intestinal fortitude. This source of strength comes directly from your spirit, which has the capacity to continuously generate positive momentum. By rehearsing yourself through these low points, you not only become stronger but also develop the intuitive paths which can connect you to these resources in the future: for fitness, work, personal challenges and other areas of life.

ON TO THE FINISH

And so we end where we began. The positive flow of energy toward the finish line is your destiny, pulling you past the challenges, through the doubts and out of the depths of uncertainty itself. You've done this yourself, and you've developed a lot more than physical capabilities along the way. That medal symbolizes a significant internal journey which has unlocked treasures that will continue to enrich you.

MAGIC WORDS

Magic words distract you from the discomfort, while they connect directly to the extra spirit that all of us have hidden inside.

*B*y using a few special words, you can pull yourself out of the downturn of motivation and physical energy that usually happens at some point during challenging workouts. I've heard from several people who, when the fatigue settled in, started to feel sorry for themselves and slow down but, through liberal magic word use, turned in a personal record or close to it. Even when your conditioning and weather conditions stop you from a fast performance, the use of these words can mentally reframe any experience into a positive one.

POSITIVE BRAINWASHING

Magic words give you another means of taking control over your performance. They allow access to the internal patterns of dealing with stress and pulling up strength which you or others have used in the past. I like to compare the network of inner connections to a mass of tangled wires, some making strength connections, some going to insecurity and negativity, and a lot of loose ends. The association of experience with words trains you to make the right connections to stay positive, deal with real problems, and pull the strength available when needed. But when used in a negative way, this ancient process is called "brainwashing."

YOU CAN USE MY WORDS, IF YOU WANT

My three magic words are *relax, power and glide*. I started using them during my competitive career to deal with three problems I encountered during difficult runs and races.

Relax: Usually at the end of a hard workout, when I feel my resources slipping away, I have a tendency to tense up under the misunderstood anxiety that things are going to get worse. With the increase in negative left brain messages due to the stress, I used to slow down and obey these messages. Now, I know that the left brain is really bluffing, making the conditions seem much worse than they really are. When I feel the first sensation of tightening, I focus on pushing beyond the stress, by saying the word "relax" to myself. After two decades of use, I now receive an instant while subtle relaxation.

Power: When I start to slow down, the left brain tells me that my strength is almost gone, bringing on a new set of brain messages from the left side, such as "You may not finish," or "Stop now before it gets worse." By merely saying the word "power," I feel a rebuilding of my strength, with the sensation that everything is going to be all right.

You don't have to give in to any negative message that hits you when you're under stress. By focusing on the positive, you maintain control. It's what you put in the forefront of your thoughts that counts.

Glide: During the latter stages of any long or hard run, my form gets shaky. To counter this trend, I say the word "glide" and instantly I feel smoother (even when I don't look any smoother). I've now associated this magic word with hundreds of runs when I started to get the "wobbles"

When you say the magic words

· You instantly feel a sense of control.

· The words first confuse and distract the left brain, cutting off the negative messages for a while.

· A surge of confidence eases in as you apply the words.

· A series of positive memories flood the subconscious and sometimes the conscious, further cutting off the left brain.

· Sometimes this series of events will jump-start the right brain, helping you find intuitive solutions to current problems.

· You relive (and are energized by) the past experiences during which you started to "lose it" but were able to focus on the positive, collecting all available resources.

· On a few occasions, you may set a personal record, finish an impossible run or pass a competitor you haven't beaten before.

· More likely, you'll be able to do what you were capable of doing on that day.

· With each use, you become more confident and effective in using your own magic.

but finished with a feeling of good form and efficiency. Now, when I say "glide," I'll receive a bit of the same sensation I felt at the end of some of my best lifetime efforts, while my pace is sometimes twice as slow.

HERE'S HOW TO MAKE YOUR WORDS MAGIC

As in any program, you must have a continual training program to develop and fine-tune these responses.

◆ Start by listing the problem areas where you could use some inner strength: relaxation, motivation, continuing under adversity, digging deeper.

◆ Go back in your memory bank and list beside each problem area, as many specific experiences as possible in which you overcame the problem.

◆ Attach a key word or phrase to each experience. The more experiences you have "cataloged" under one of these keys, the more powerful their effect.

◆ Each time you overcome one of these problems again, add a new experience to the category and attach the key word to it.

As you add more experiences, the magic of the words becomes more powerful. You're training your organism to set in motion the same complex set of reactions which produced the success in the past. Not only does this help to mobilize the elements which can get the job done. Intuitively, you set in motion a search for the many little connections inside which give you a realistic feeling of control and power.

87

> **"I know I would have gone 15 minutes slower, at least, if I hadn't used the magic words you told me about."**

Use these as needed to take off the pressure and bring back the confidence. Add more key words and the accompanying thoughts which make sense to you. Subtract items which don't engage you. You are molding this to fit your needs like a glove.

RELAX

- There's no pressure on me; I'm here to have fun.
- I'm going slow. If it gets tough, I'll just slow down more.
- From the first step, I'm going to relax and enjoy the endorphins.
- I feel comfortable, supported by all of the energy.
- I'm part of a very positive movement.

POWER

- I feel good about myself and what I'm doing.
- This experience gives me control over myself.
- I know what I'm doing when I'm out here.
- This is my heritage; the power of the human migration spirit is with me.

ACHIEVEMENT

- I've developed great self respect through this event and the training.
- I created this level of fitness, and I'm very proud of it.
- Each step is giving me benefits.
- This achievement builds upon a long series of successes.

I'M STORING ENERGY

- I've got all day—enjoy!
- Slow down and savor this moment.
- Store this energy away.

WALKING AND SHUFFLING EXTENDS RESOURCES

- The walk/shuffle breaks push back my wall.
- Every person who passes me is pulling me along.
- This side of the road is my walk/shuffle break lane; I own it.
- Walk/shuffle breaks give power.
- Walk/shuffle breaks are my heritage.
- I only have _____ more minutes/seconds (until the next break).
- Walk/shuffle breaks hold back the energy tide so it will surge at the end.

NO PROBLEMS WILL GET TO ME

- I've got all the resources I need.
- Everyone feels discomfort.
- I'm hanging in there.
- I'm working through this.
- The problem is easing; it's going away.
- I can slow down and feel better.
- I can shorten my stride and relax the muscles.

The words aren't magic in themselves. They come alive and make better connections as you associate each with experiences in which you overcame specific problems. The more experiences, the more magic.

MUSCLES—LISTEN TO ME!

- I'm shortening stride and shuffling.
- Movement pulls out the cramp.
- The muscle is loosening up.

I LOVE HILLS!

- All the power is there to zoom up this hill, but I'm going to save it.
- I'll shorten stride down to "baby steps," if needed.
- I'm low to the ground and feeling light on my feet.
- My muscles are relaxing; I've got the strength.
- The hill is working with me to pull me up.

SHORT (STRIDE) IS BETTER

- I'm shortening stride and feeling more power.
- Just a little stride-shortening makes the muscles relax.
- This shorter stride gives me more control.
- Every time I shorten stride, I decrease my chance of injury.
- With a shorter stride, I can turn over my legs better.

I'M GETTING THERE!

- I'm tired but strong.
- I'm feeling better.
- I'm tired but proud.

- There's plenty of strength left.
- The reward is coming.
- What a wonderful accomplishment!
- Less than 2 tenths of one per cent of the population can do this—I'm doing it!
- Tight legs are a sign of accomplishment; I'll shorten my stride and run smooth.

WARNING: YOUR WORDS WILL LOSE THEIR MAGIC, IF YOU USE THEM IN A LEFT BRAIN WAY.

Some exercisers can get a quick fix by using the word "power," for example, to pick up the pace for a hundred meters or so in the middle of a race. This will almost always lead to a significant slowdown at the end.

Magic words gradually program your internal systems to pull together in an instant the complex series of internal connections which produced success in past experiences. The invoking of an isolated word to dramatically turn around the natural effects of fatigue can increase speed for a short distance, while saving up valuable resources that you need...in the long run.

DIRTY TRICKS

*"**W**hen I was feeling at the end of my resources, at mile 24, I tried one of your dirty mental tricks. It gave me a sense of...control, and I ran the last mile with a smile on my face".*

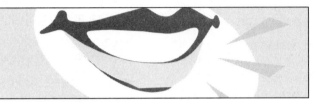

A really good rehearsal (with good pace judgment) will pull you most of the way through the race. By adding some magic words, you'll push two to five miles further, sometimes all the way to the finish line. But there are moments in every race, usually near the end, when the magic seems to have gone out of your words, and worse, your legs. This opens up a big microphone into which the left brain shouts its messages. You've probably heard most of them:

"It's over. Just walk to the finish."

"Slow down; it'll feel much better."

"Stop now and feel great."

"Oh, do I feel bad."

"I can't do it today."

(And the worst one of all) "Why am I doing this?"

It's time to play some dirty tricks on your left brain, After all, it does this to you all the time. You're only in trouble if you listen to them. Dirty tricks distract the left brain so that you can get further down the road. But they can do so much more.

As you find a series of creative images which get you into your right brain, you'll trigger other imaginative thoughts. These may entertain you, but they are most effective when they jump-start right brain activity, which produces intuitive solutions to problems. It keeps probing, hitting dead ends and trying again until it finds the direct connections to the centers that get the job done. In addition, right brain activity improves motivation and keeps your organism working all the way to the finish.

If you've trained according to the schedules in this book and pace yourself realistically in the race itself, you will be physically on the express train to the finish. There is, however, a very real mental wall which most exercisers must push through to get through the last few miles. By doing your mental training homework, you'll push the wall closer and closer to the finish.

Just as leg and overall physical fatigue is delayed by regular shifts in running and walking form, mental freshness is maintained by shifts back and forth between the left and right brain. Mental strength is developed through rehearsal and use of your magic words. As you increase the ease of shifting into the right brain, you'll delay even further the point in the race where your attitude won't respond.

Dirty tricks are reserved for that aggravating place, late in the event, when a growing stream of mental email bombs from the left brain attack your will to go on.

Almost everybody gets these messages or worse. You're only in trouble if you listen to them and believe them. Dirty tricks help by distracting the left brain for a few moments so that you can get further down the road. As you find a series of creative images which activate the right brain, you will trigger other imaginative thoughts. These can become visions which will entertain you and may unlock creative solutions to problems, activate motivation and keep you exercising to capacity all the way to the finish line.

Dirty tricks are merely crazy ideas which can't be grasped by the left brain because they are not logical. Let's go through one of these so that you can see the dynamic aspects of their effects.

Even without this marvelous performance enhancement band, we have the capacity inside to go faster. Because we're under maximum stress at this point, the left brain is in control. Dirty tricks allow you to break free for a while.

TWO MAJOR ROLES FOR DIRTY TRICKS

* *Sneak down the road while the left brain is confused*

   The left brain, in all of its logic, doesn't know what to do with "a giant, invisible rubber band." While it is befuddled, you have a window of opportunity for avoiding negative messages and moving toward your goal. The more you get into the vision of the dirty trick, the more

time you'll have before the negative side starts spewing its venom again. You may get 100, 200 or 400 meters down the road. But the finish line is only a series of dirty trick segments away.

* *One crazy thought can unlock another*

   Even one imaginative dirty trick can start the creative side of the brain working on other interesting images, visions and notions which will entertain you and get you closer to the finish.

   More significantly, a series of these "tricks" can unlock inside you the creative process itself, which can mobilize all of your resources in overcoming challenges and getting you to the finish line feeling good.

   The best dirty tricks are the ones that work for you. Only you will respond to the unique chemistry of specific images and crazy concepts. Start concocting these during your right brain runs and remember the ones that work. The more you use them, the more effective they become.

   Almost any imaginative idea will distract you for a while. To engage the performance components inside, it helps if the "tricks" are related to behaviors which help you in your event. Here are a few ideas that have worked for me:

* *Oxygen molecules*

   The night before a race, I collect several million oxygen molecules in a sandwich bag and pin it on my shorts. During the latter stages of the event, when the oxygen doesn't seem to be as abundant, I take off the bag and squeeze it out in front of my mouth or nose. Before squeezing, I exhale completely every third or fourth breath. Just one or two

91

Jeff Galloway's Giant Invisible Rubber Band

On all marathons, I carry with me this device, which is mounted to my shorts in the small of my back. When someone passes me in the late stages, my left brain explodes with a stream of negative messages, such as "Look how smooth he/ she is running, and how ragged you are." It's easy to listen and give in to those logical messages which are trying to reduce my effort and slow me down.

But instead of believing this source of lazy and distractive ideas, I attack by throwing the giant band over the head of the individual who had the audacity to pass me. For a while, the lead may grow. During the next few hundred yards, I fill in a great number of details, such as imagining how the tension on the rubber band is increasing, cutting off oxygen supply to the brain of the person I "rubber banded." The hope develops that he or she will have to slow down.

At some point I must laugh at myself for believing in such a ridiculous device. But laughing helps to send me into the right side of my brain, and I relax. Limber legs turn over quicker, and I usually catch up with, or pass, the person that passed me.

The giant invisible rubber band worked again!

92

squeezes last about 100 to 200 yards. The best part of this trick will be seeing and hearing the reactions from the people around you. If you're a real salesperson, you may try to make some money from the severely oxygen-deprived folks who went out too fast. Just bring along some extra bags.

- *Ball Bearing Atoms*

This is a high-tech right brain invention which will send you gliding to the finish. As the legs lose their resiliency near the finish, you can shake off of your hair millions of atoms which normally act to help it shiny. As they drop on to your shoes and feet, you'll find that you don't need to stretch out your stride any more. You glide better through the air and stay economically more efficient by staying closer to the ground. When you're losing this effect, shake your hair again. Balding people, like myself, will always appreciate some strategic head shakes from others. A downhill portion of the course will enhance the effect of these virtually invisible ball bearings.

- *A Giant Hand*

The ancient Greeks often imagined that Zeus or another god was helping them in difficult situations. When it becomes tough to go up a hill during those last few miles, call for the giant hand to come in and gently push you up. Most folks find that the hand comes in gently as you get your posture upright. The support increases as you shorten stride, keep feet low to the ground, and let the feet gently lift off when they are directly underneath you.

- *Your "Inspiration" Shoes*

If logistics permit, you might consider changing shoes during the last six miles of the race. Both shoes must be broken in, of course. Save your "inspirational" pair for the last part. Just putting them on sends a jolt of invigoration into your feet, up your legs, then through your body and into the right brain. At that point, all types of crazy and innovative things can happen.

♦ *The Energy Bar Boost*

For the long distance journey, you're not bringing just any energy bar. Pick the ones with the greatest energy potential from your most powerful stash of bars and infuse them with even more energy. Handle the pieces of these bars with care as you don't want to infect everyone around you. As you chew on each piece and drink water you feel the energy move from your mouth to your right brain. Then, instantly it unlocks other pockets of energy which have been hiding until that point.

Have fun with these dirty tricks. Since your only constraint is the imaginative power of your right brain, there are no limits to what you can unleash.

RECOVERY AND BEYOND

RACE RECOVERY

*E*ven if the race distance is twice as far as you've ever raced before in your life, you can be back to your normal exercise routine very quickly by following a few simple steps, before and after your race. By mentally and physically preparing for the morning after, you can reduce the negatives, while emotionally riding the wave of positive momentum from even the toughest of races.

THE POST-RACE LETDOWN

Even with the best preparation, however, there will be a natural motivational lull. When you've spent months working toward a specific event and you've reached the finish line of a significant physical test, even the most focused athletes experience a psychological letdown. The challenge has motivated you to be regular with your exercise, to keep pushing your endurance limits on long ones and to reach down deep for motivation and the strength to go on. Like most unique lifetime accomplishments, the day of achievement is an emotional peak day, followed by a downturn. As soon as you fully grasp the reality that the "accomplishment doldrums" will occur, you can prepare for them and desensitize yourself to the negative effects. Talk yourself through this: "It's natural, after six months of preparation for the big day, to miss the focus, the

commitment and the reinforcement of others who supported me in my mission." But you can also tell yourself with honesty that in a few days you can be shrugging off the blues as you strike out in a new direction. So... let's get another mission started, NOW!

SELECT ANOTHER "MISSION" BEFORE THE BIG DAY

Write the date of your next project on a calendar, journal, etc. The farther ahead of your first goal, the better. It's best to shift gears in selecting a different type of mission: a scenic trail, a weekend trip to a big festival event, a group run or walk with friends you haven't seen for a while, etc. If you've trained in a group, schedule an easy workout three to four weeks after the race, and you'll look forward to the reunion. It's okay to shift missions in midstream, but be sure to have a specific event always written on the calendar. If you wait until after your first "mission day" to choose another goal, your letdown will be more severe.

THE BODY FOLLOWS YOUR MENTAL VISION

The more you embrace your new mission in advance, the quicker you'll lose the aches and pains of the big race. Instead of wallowing in your misery, tell yourself that your muscles have achieved their "good tired-ness" by overcoming a great challenge—and you're still glowing from it. The positive mental momentum from your accomplish-ment will pull you through the few days immediately after when you may (or may not) feel that the legs don't want to go a step. Read this section several times before your event, mentally rehearsing each of the elements.

A FEW SECONDS OF PATIENCE...

If your pace in the early miles is conserva-tive, you'll recover a lot faster. You'll also go faster at the end of the race than you would have. When the first few miles are even 10 seconds too fast, you'll often slow down 30 to 60 seconds/mile at the end. By going out 10 to 20 seconds slower than you could go in the first few miles, you'll pass more people at the end, pick up the pace, have a faster time and recover in at least half the time.

HYDRATE AND AVOID SALT AND ALCOHOL

During the 36-hour period before your big race, look at the labels of products you eat and avoid those that have any significant salt content. It's also best to watch the food you eat in restaurants because most kitchens put significant amounts of salt in almost everything. Drink 6 to 8 ounces of water or electrolyte beverage every hour you're awake, until you hear sloshing in your stomach. I like to drink up to a quart of an electrolyte drink on the day before a an event. Rehearse this hydration plan on the long ones leading up to your event, and you'll have your program set for your goal event weekend.

AT THE FINISH LINE

Even if you don't want to, keep walking after you cross the finish. Grab two cups of water, drink and keep walking. Get two more cups and pour them on your legs and two more on your head if you feel hot. Walk to the food area, pick up your carbo-hydrate snacks of choice and eat, while you continue drinking water or electrolyte bever-age. Keep walking for a mile or so—your legs will recover faster because the walking pumps new blood in there, pushing the waste products out.

THROUGHOUT THE AFTERNOON

After a meal and a shower, walk for 2 to 4 more miles very easily—just keep the legs moving. Drink water, electrolyte beverages, citrus juice and eat some lowfat protein with other carbohydrates. You've earned your food rewards, and you'll reload most effec-tively when you've eaten a good small meal within 30 minutes after the finish. You don't have to be a pig, just keep snacking all af-ternoon and evening. For the next few days, you may want to increase your consump-tion of vitamin C to speed up healing of little micro-tears in your muscles and tendons.

THE NEXT DAY

Walk for 30 to 60 minutes or more. The pace can be as slow as you wish, just keep moving. If you have soreness, the walking will work it out quicker than sitting on a couch.

RUNNERS: TWO DAYS AFTER—YOUR RETURN TO EXERCISE DAY

Start by walking for 5 to 10 minutes. Then, insert a 30 to 60 second run break every 3 to 5 minutes. Stay out there for 20 to 30 minutes, adjusting the walking and running so that you feel comfortable and are not straining. The return to short segments of

96

gentle running will speed up the recovery of race-weary muscles.

RUNNERS: CONTINUE TO ALTERNATE RUN DAYS WITH WALK DAYS

Over the next two weeks, continue to walk 30 to 60 minutes one day, followed by a day of walk-running for 30 to 60 minutes. Gradually increase the running portions. Four days after the race, for example, you could try walking three minutes and jogging two to three minutes. Two days later, you may be back to running three minutes and walking one minute. Don't push yourself and you'll recover faster.

TAKE ONE WEEK OFF FROM RACING AND SPEED TRAINING FOR EVERY SIX MILES OF THE RACE

After a half or full marathon, don't race for at least five weeks. You could schedule a short race three weeks after a half marathon. Even if you're feeling great, a 5K race too soon after a marathon or half marathon can leave you more fatigued than you felt after your big race and cause injury.

WEEKEND WORKOUTS CAN GRADUALLY INCREASE IN DISTANCE

For races between 5K and 15K, you may resume long sessions either the weekend after the race or the one following. A race longer than 15K up to 30K, such as a half marathon, will require a two to three-week vacation from long distance workouts. From the 15 K (9+ miles for the half)or 30K (18+ miles for the full) distance and beyond, the long one can be done three to four weeks after the race and every third week thereafter. As you resume long ones, be sure to pace them according to the pacing section for long ones.

Marathon runners/walkers have the option of waiting three or four weeks before resuming long ones. The distances recommended for the other weekends: is 4 to 6 miles, then 6 to 8 miles, followed by either a long one of 12 to 21 miles or an easy 5 to 10 miles (if your long one is scheduled the following weekend).

IF YOU'VE DONE A HALF OR FULL MARATHON AND WANT TO DO ANOTHER ONE IN THE NEAR FUTURE...

First, make sure that you're recovered. Once you've gone 9+ miles (half) or 18+ (full), you can maintain this level, or increase your limit, by going at least 9 miles every other weekend (half) or 18 miles every third weekend (full). Those who will do a half or full marathon six weeks after their first event would do 13 to 14 miles (half) (23 to 26 for full) three weeks after their first event. If there are more than 6 to 7 weeks between events, count back from event day. Then, look at the training schedule in this book for the chosen distance and count back to schedule the weekend workouts.

THE GROUP WILL PULL YOU THROUGH

The fun and the bonding that occurs inside a training group will keep you going and can make training fun. When you have a choice, pick a group that goes at a pace that is very comfortable. By exercising totally within yourself, you'll be able to tell jokes and even remember some of the better ones. *(Visit www.JeffGalloway.com "training groups" to locate the nearest group or ask for the information to start your own.)*

THE "MARATHON A MONTH" CLUB

A growing number of marathoners are choosing to do their training run in a different city's event each month. The self-proclaimed members of this fictitious club enjoy the travel with a mission and the different personality of each marathon. By doing these at least two minutes per mile slower than one could run on that day, inserting all walk breaks, there is little risk of injury.

ABOVE ALL...

Don't get carried away. Enjoy your accomplishment and have fun with your exercise. If you go slowly enough, you can recover quickly and receive all of the satisfaction of your long training sessions and races.

Before and during: The little things which speed recovery

- Start conservatively. Time goal runners should start the race 10 to 20 seconds slower than you could run on that day for at least the first 15 to 20 percent of the race (3 to 6 miles in a marathon, 2 to 3 for the half). First-timers should go one to two minutes per mile slower than the fast race pace predicted by the "magic mile." At best, during the second half, you can choose to speed up or to finish within your capacity for a faster recovery. Even if it happens to be a hot, humid, bad day, you won't slow down as much at the end if you've started conservatively.

- Avoid alcohol and salt and limit caffeine during the 36 hours before the big day. In addition, drink 6 to 8 ounces of water or electrolyte beverage.

- Take every walk/shuffle break, from the beginning, and pace yourself conservatively accounting for heat, humidity, hills and other factors.

- Don't overstride at any time. Without knowing it, many exercisers are so exuberant in the beginning that they lengthen their stride too far, overextending the muscles. More damage occurs from overstriding at the end of long workout sessions and races—especially half or full marathons. Try very hard to rein in your stride as you go downhill. Studies continue to show that you'll go faster and recover faster when you keep your feet low to the ground, have a short stride and stay light on your feet.

- Have an energy gel, pieces of energy bars, etc. all the way to the end, during the second half of a workout that will last 90 minutes or more. Most exercisers should start taking these "boosters" after 60 to 80 minutes on all long workouts to find the frequency and quantity of product which you need during the long events. Be sure to drink water when you take these products.

- Drink at every water stop unless you hear sloshing in your stomach but don't drink more than 27 oz. an hour.

THE BIG DAY: YOU STILL HAVE A CHANCE TO ASSUME CONTROL

THE BIG DAY: IMPROVING PERFORMANCE WITHOUT TRAINING

THE LAST 48 HOURS

While the physical training has been done, you can significantly enhance 1) the way you feel afterward and 2) the quality of your performance by choosing certain behaviors and avoiding others during the final two days. Graduation day is near; don't let your vision get cloudy.

FOCUS

Because of nervousness, the excitement of the expo and the distractions of another city, the race, friends, etc., it's easy to lose concentration on a few key items. Be sure to read this section over several times during the last few weeks so that you're more likely to keep the mind and body on track.

YOU'RE IN CONTROL

You need to be in charge of your behaviors during the last 48 hours. In this way you can control your attitude, your eating, your schedule, etc. This doesn't mean that you should stay by yourself in a hotel room eating salt-free pretzels and energy bars and drinking water. Being with friends is positive. You have veto power over what goes into your mouth, where you go and how late you stay out.

BE POSITIVE

Have a list of statements, similar to the ones in the "Magic Words" section of this book, which you can repeat as necessary. You're going to have negative thoughts slip out from the left brain so we'll work on a way to bypass them and move into the world of the positive.

- I have no pressure on myself.

- I'm going to enjoy this.

- I'll start very slowly.

- The people are great.

- Because I started slowly, I'm finishing strong.

- The satisfaction of doing this is unequaled.

- I've developed a great respect for myself.

DRINK!

During the 48 hours before the race, drink at least 4 to 6 ounces of water every hour you're awake. If you're sweating, drink more. If you prefer to drink juices or electrolyte beverages, then do so.

AVOID THE DEHYDRATING ELEMENTS

Alcohol: During the 36-hour period before the race, it's best to avoid alcohol completely. Your exercising muscles and kidneys will thank you for abstaining the day and night before the race.

Caffeine: For those who dearly love their cup of coffee on race morning... go ahead. But make it just one cup, and drink a glass of water before or afterward.

Salt: This is probably the leading dehydrating agent for most endurance athletes. Because it's used so widely in the preparation of most restaurant food, you're likely to consume large amounts of it when you're away from home without realizing it. For this reason:

1. Try to avoid restaurant food during the 18-hour period before the race.

2. Eat foods which you know do not contain salt (or are very low in salt).

3. Drink a little more water than normal if you've consumed food which you suspect has some salt in it.

Even one salty meal the night before a race will leave you significantly dehydrated for the race itself—no matter how much water you drink. So if you go to the pasta-loading party the night before, watch out for the sauce and the garlic bread! (Just nibble on the pasta and digest the conversation.)

MEDICATIONS

Most medications (especially those for colds, flu, etc.) have a dehydrating effect. Be sure to consult with a doctor (who supports and knows the various effects of running) to adjust your medication accordingly.

EAT!

The best eating plan for the 48-hour race countdown is the best eating plan for life in general: keep eating nonfat snacks continually, all day long. Avoid eating a large solid-food meal the afternoon or evening before.

So if you want to snack on energy bars all afternoon or have a series of carbohydrate snacks which you know will get through your system quickly, do so. Concentrated forms of sugar (frozen yogurt, syrup, candy) are not recommended.

CHECK OUT THE STAGING AREA

If it is possible, go over the staging area the day before. As a guide, it's great to have someone who has run that race before: he or she will probably know where you'll be arriving, where to keep warm and relax, and the best way to get to the portion of the road where you'll be lining up. If you get a clear idea of all this ahead of time, you'll feel more in control and will tend to receive fewer left brain messages.

REST

You don't have to sleep, but you should rest. Settle into your home or hotel room and relax in the best way you know. Read, watch TV, listen to music, talk with friends... but relax. Again, take control of your environment and mold for yourself a positive and cozy atmosphere. Don't worry if you don't sleep at all, but lay that head down and store up some energy.

101

WAKE UP

Set your wake-up call so that you have plenty of time to get moving, gather your gear together and go through your usual eating and drinking timetable which worked for you during the long ones.

DRINK REGULARLY BUT NOT TOO MUCH (14-27 OZ AN HOUR)

Before long training sessions, test various patterns of fluid intake to avoid bathroom stops. Most exercisers find that drinking about 8-10 oz, 2-3 hours before the start will allow time to get the fluid out of the system. The best pattern, however is that which works for you. During long workouts and the race, the advice (from the medical teams of the major marathons) is to drink 14-27 oz an hour. For most, this averages to about 4 oz every 1-2 miles. Water tends to cause fewer problems for most. (One oz. is around 30 ml.)

EAT—TO HOLD YOUR BLOOD SUGAR UP FOR THE FIRST HALF

One of the reasons I've advocated eating before all of your long ones is to discover the foods and the pattern of eating which will work best for you in the race itself.

Eating about 200 to 250 calories of high quality carbohydrate about an hour before a long one has helped many racers to stablize their blood sugar level for the first half. If you've experienced an upset stomach when eating before, start your blood sugar boosters earlier and don't eat before the start.

RUNNERS: GO SLOWLY IN THE BEGINNING

Almost everyone who performs a personal record in the longer events does the second half faster than the first. Slow down by 10 to 20 seconds per mile (from your projected pace) during the first three to five miles, and then follow the guidelines in the "Pacing Tips" chapter which follows this one. Many report that by starting out 15 seconds per mile slower, they have the resiliency to run 20 to 30 seconds per mile faster at the end of the run.

RUNNERS: TAKE WALK BREAKS

A high percentage of those who didn't achieve the time goal they desired in the half or full marathon by running continuously have been able to significantly improve finishing times by walking according to the table in the Run-Walk-Run chapter.

EAT DURING THE RACE

Eating blood sugar-boosting snacks, starting at about six miles has helped exercisers improve time goals by boosting the blood sugar level. This maintains mental concentration, sustains a positive mental attitude, and reduces the opportunity for negative left brain messages to creep in. Be sure to re-read the "Food and Fatburning" section in this book—especially the "blood sugar boosters" section. Don't try any new food on race day.

HAVE FUN!

You have almost complete control over the way you will feel after the race by conservative pacing and frequent walk/shuffle breaks from the beginning. By staying within your physical capabilities throughout the first 70 percent of the race, you can enjoy the people, the joking, the sights, and the overall experience...as you are rewarded with the feeling of accomplishment. Be gentle on yourself throughout the race and the enjoyment will flow. For sharing purposes, don't forget to bring with you the following: a joke, an interesting story, a controversial issue and/or some gossip. Of course, bring along anything else like this that doesn't weigh much and will add to the fun.

RACE DAY CHECKLIST

THE DAY BEFORE

- Drink 4 to 6 ounces of water every hour.

- Mentally rehearse the race, feeling good, overcoming challenges, recovering.

- Eat small carbohydrate snacks constantly.

- Relax with friends or family.

THE NIGHT BEFORE

- Drink 4 to 6 ounces of water every hour.

- Eat light carbohydrate snacks like energy bars.

- Relax, laugh, enjoy the moment.

- Go over the procedure, route, etc. for getting to the start.

- Do a very relaxed mental rehearsal of the event, concentrating on the positive.

- Pack your bag.

YOUR RACE BAG SHOULD CONTAIN:

- Race number and pins

- Race instructions, map, etc.

- Copy this "Race Day Checklist." (next page) and a copy of "Magic Words"

- Prepare to bring a controversial issue, at least one interesting story and at least one joke

- Shoes, socks, shirt, shorts and warm-up suit

- Other clothes if it's cold: tights, polypro top, long-sleeved T, gloves, hat, ear covering, etc.

- Water (about 32 to 64 oz.)

- Bandages, Vaseline, etc.

- $20-30 for reserve funds (rapid transit tokens, etc.)

- Energy bars or your chosen blood sugar boosting source (enough for start, second half and after)

- Fanny pack or plastic bags, pins

- Some extra "give-away" shirts and/or pants as extra layers in case staging area is cold

- Garbage bags as an inexpensive waterproof top and ground cover

"RACE MORNING LIST"

- Drink 4 to 6 oz. of water every 30 minutes until you hear "sloshing." Cut off fluid intake according to what has worked before long ones.

- Eat—according to the schedule which has worked for you in the long ones. (example: one energy bar with 8 oz. water, 1 to 2 hours before the start)

- Bring your bag, car keys, etc.

- Leave at least 30 minutes before you think you'll need to leave...in case of traffic, etc.

- If you have several hours at the race site before start, stay warm, get off your feet and relax.

- Sixty minutes before the start, walk around the staging area to mentally rehearse lining up.

- Thirty minutes before the start, walk around for 15 minutes to get the legs moving.

- Jog or walk for 3 to 5 minutes (very slowly) just before lining up.

- Keep the legs moving, in place if necessary as you stand waiting for the start.

- If going for a time goal, get to the starting area early enough to secure a good place.

- Most of us with the goal "to finish" should line up in the back of the crowd.

- Joke around; enjoy the energy and personalities of the folks nearby.

- Go out slowly. If it's hot, go out even slower!

- Get over to the side of the road and take every walk or shuffle break, from the beginning.

- Drink at every water station until you hear sloshing in your stomach. (No more than 27 oz. per hour!)

- If you feel warm, pour water over your head at each water stop.

- Each walk or shuffle break gives you a chance to appreciate and enjoy each mile.

- When tired, shorten your stride.

- Don't stretch during or immediately afterward, unless you've found help from certain stretches.

- You may cut out the walk or shuffle breaks after mile 18 in the marathon/9 miles in the half if you're feeling good.

IMMEDIATELY AFTERWARD:

- Grab water and carbohydrate food(s).

- Walk, eat and drink, for at least a mile.

RECOVERY:

- If possible, immerse your legs in a cold bath, as soon after the finish as possible.

- Within 30 minutes, eat around 200 calories of 80% carb/20% protein.

- Walk for 30 to 60 minutes later in the day.

- Eat snacks continuously for the rest of the day.

- Drink 4 to 6 oz. of water or electrolyte fluid (at least) every hour.

- Walk for 30 to 60 minutes the next day.

- Run/walk for 30 to 45 minutes two days after the event.

- Continue to alternate: walk 30 to 60 minutes and run/walk 30 to 45 minutes.

- Wait at least a week before you 1) schedule your next race or 2) vow never to do another.

PACING TIPS FOR RUNNERS

*F*irst-time marathoners should run at the training pace or slower for the first 18 miles at least. For first-time half marathoners, make it 7-10 miles. At any time after that point, you may increase your speed if you feel strong and wish to do so.

TIME GOAL RUNNERS

- **For the first 3 to 5 miles,** run 10 to 20 sec/mile slower than goal pace during the running parts and take the walk breaks.

- A one-minute walk break (for the average person) will slow you by 15 to 18 seconds.

- A slightly slower pace for the first 3 to 5 miles will allow the legs to warm up before pushing into race effort.

- Remember to adjust your pace for heat, humidity and hills. (30 sec/mi slower for every 5 degrees above 60˚ F)

- **Between 5 and 8 miles,** shift to running faster in the running portions and take the walk breaks, gradually moving up to goal pace.

- You will gradually pick up the pace so that by eight miles, you're running at goal pace when you average the walk breaks and the running segments.

- If it's a struggle to pick up the pace, stay at an effort level which is comfortable.

- Don't even think about cutting your walk break short to speed things up.

- **Between 8 and 18 miles,** run at goal pace (run faster to compensate for walk breaks). Half marathoners try to maintain pace to the finish.

- Stay smooth as you ease down to walk and ease back into running.

- Compute your pace each mile – and adjust. It helps to have a pace chart.

- Uphill miles can be slower, and downhill miles can be faster than goal pace.

- **After 18 miles (9 miles for half marathoners),** marathoners can cut out the walk breaks when feeling strong.

- An alternative: walk for 30 seconds for several walk breaks before eliminating them.

- If you need the breaks but legs are cramping, shuffle instead of walking.

- **After 23 miles (11 for the half),** you can keep picking up the pace if you feel up to it.

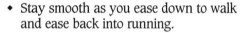

Note: See the Predicting Race Performance chapter in this book.

RUNNERS: A FASTER RACE

BEFORE YOU ATTEMPT A TIME GOAL... READ THIS

THE MANY WAYS TO "WIN" A RACE

There are an almost unlimited number of different race "missions." Each can enrich your life in a different way, while delivering about the same exhilaration as received the first time.

Over the past 30 years, I must have compared notes with over 150,000 veterans. A few continue to focus exclusively on running the fastest time they can run, every event. But almost every veteran, even those with over 100 completion medals, will put at the top of the rewards, the unique feeling of satisfaction experienced every time you cross the finish line.

The most important concept you can grasp as you get into the running lifestyle is that you are the captain of your ship. You'll get a lot of advice about how you should run and what you should do next. Pick a good, conservative program, like the one in this book and learn to have fun following it. When you take too many elements from too many different types of programs, you can decrease your chance of success and enjoyment. At the same time, a "combo" program will increase your chance of injury.

WHY RUN FASTER?

Good question! When the benefits are few and the challenges significant and many, you must answer this question before and throughout the program to maintain consistent motivation. Every person needs to dig down and come up with his or her own answer. I'll give you mine.

While most of the enduring and life-changing benefits from the race experience come only from finishing, there are a few unique life-enhancing capabilities to be gained from testing yourself in a time goal program. It's possible to get all of the benefit from this test, even if you don't do the projected race. It's also possible, though unusual to have the good genes and/or luck to run a fast time and receive none of the good internal engineering.

Finishing a long event forces everyone to bring mind and body together and to reach for extra resources from the power of the human spirit. A time goal program goes one step farther than finishing, putting you on the edge of endurance and strength almost every week. In this process, you will invariably find weakness and setbacks. As you pull yourself out of the rut, you must question your resolve and your spirit, readjust and come back stronger. Almost every one of the time goal runners I've communicated with has been recharged by the challenge with a better understanding of who they are, as people. And many of these apply the lessons to other areas of life.

DON'T ATTEMPT A TIME GOAL UNTIL YOU HAVE RUN AT LEAST ONE RACE

Even veteran runners will learn some very important lessons in their first race at any distance. Everyone can have a really good experience in their first long distance event if they start slowly and keep the pace comfortable throughout. A good first-time goal should be a pace that is about 2 minutes slower per mile than you could run the same distance when racing, according to the "magic mile" time trial.

108 SO WHAT IS A REALISTIC GOAL?

Use the "magic mile" noted in the Predicting Race Performance chapter.

If it's your first race, add 2 min/mi to the adjusted prediction time. If you have run the distance before and want to finish feeling good, add 30 to 60 sec/mi to that predicted time.

LIMIT YOUR TIME GOAL RACES

There are many negative consequences to setting a goal on that is too challenging. If you enjoy the competition and the satisfaction of achieving a specific goal, then one or two races a year (at most) could be set aside for this purpose. The best reward for this hard work is the Boston Marathon.

Qualifying for Boston is one of the greatest accomplishments in a runner's life. The experience of that special weekend, during which over a million people cheer you with unique intensity, will be something you'll remember for the rest of your life.

Before committing to a time goal program, be sure to evaluate the risk-reward ratio. To finish a race requires very little interruption in your lifestyle. The extra time required for a time goal, however, can take its toll on family, career and other areas of life. Training "to finish" takes about one third to one-half the time required by most time goal runners. The extra mileage and speed training will also produce more aches, pains, doubts, negative messages and, possibly, injuries.

There is a high burnout rate among time goal racers. They often become so focused on the goal that they miss the joy of the body responding to an early morning run or the glow of a trail at sunset. If the satisfaction is focused solely on the clock at the finish, most of the joys of running slip by, underappreciated. One reason for the high rate of failure of time goal runners in hitting a specific goal is that they have no control over several of the primary reasons for slowing down in a race: temperature, humidity, course difficulty and congestion of a crowded event.

If you include running fun, every week, and you're flexible about your goal, you have a chance to achieve a time goal...and a life too. At least two of your long runs could be done in other races, gradually building up to the fast one (observe the Two-Minute Rule!). If the weather or your body doesn't cooperate on goal day, don't thrash yourself. Drop out before mile 18 in the marathon (9 miles in the half) and you can usually recover fairly quickly. This allows for another race in a few weeks.

THE ROLE OF THE SLOW RACE

I've run over 70 marathons the recreational way. By running slower than I could run, from the beginning, the marathon becomes enjoyable. I ran Boston with my father in 1996, after having run it four other times.

Since I was going along comfortably, I enjoyed the course and was surprised to recognize very little of it. Each of the other efforts were fiercely competitive. I hardly noticed anything but the clock, my competitors and how I felt. It was so much better in '96, savoring the landmarks, the people and the time with my Dad.

The more significantly you back off from what you could run, the better you'll feel during the race and the more likely it will be that you'll remember what went on. You'll expand the number of possible running companions and open yourself up for a number of "fun" missions, listed below.

MISSIONS

Time goal variations: Time goals don't have to be gut-wrenching. Here are a few that have energized myself and others. Don't stop with these ideas. Be creative and you'll look forward to every one.

- **Set up a predicted time,** one that you know you could do. Tell your friends about it and see if they want to have a pool. The winner and the racer, you, get a free celebration dinner.

- **Running no faster than...** This is particularly a good idea for those who find it hard to slow down. Reward yourself for running slower than a certain time. This has helped hundreds of runners to learn how to hold back and enjoy the company of those farther back in the pack.

OTHER MISSIONS

Helping a charity A growing number of runners find it fulfilling to raise money for a charity that means something to them. Many charities have programs that allow donors to deduct the contributions, while the runner earns a free trip to a great race. I support the Marathon To Fight Breast Cancer (breastcancermarathon.com), which includes a half marathon.

Running with a relative I've heard it said numerous times that there's no better way to see relatives in a positive light than to train with and then run/walk a race together. The bonding is impossible to describe. When you live in different cities, the phone contact throughout the training keeps you in touch and your relationship alive.

Mentoring someone who really needs it At race expos, I talk with folks who are reunited by training for and running/walking an event together. Maybe you want to reconnect with a college roommate going through a divorce or introduce a high school best friend to your training buddies. It could be a former mentor of yours who has lost fitness and focus and is looking for both. Long distance event training helps people restart their lives (or reconnect) in a positive way.

50-staters After running five to 10 marathons or halfs, some new racers like the challenge and the travel. So they set out on a five to 10-year goal to run a race in every state. This has been extended to all continents, Canadian provinces, etc. Whatever makes sense to you is an appropriate mission!

Revisit a special place It could be the town where you or your father grew up, went to college, started your career...whatever is interesting to you.

109

A scavenger hunt If someone in your group knows the course, you can set up a scavenger hunt. Buy souvenirs from certain parts of town on the course, wear pieces of clothing from distinctive stores, or take a "throwaway" camera and get pictures of yourself with landmarks on the course for proof. Your imagination is your only limit.

Sightseeing, with a list Carry a little notepad and pen in your fanny pack and note the historical and scenic points on the course. Try to find something about each area that most people would overlook. This gives you a creative task during walk breaks. Compare notes with friends at your victory celebration afterward.

QUESTIONS ABOUT SLOW MARATHONS:

"I've tried to run a race slowly, and I became more sore than I was after a fast one."

If you're getting sore or feeling more effort when going slowly, you're running inefficiently. By shortening your stride and keeping the feet low to the ground, you incur very little exertion. In this very efficient running mode, your main running muscles are mostly resting.

I've talked to several fast runners who seem to be running correctly, yet still became sore after a marathon. After a few more questions, however, I learned that they went into the marathon with a long run of only 19, 16, or, in one case, 12 miles. Whenever you ask your body to go that much further than you have gone in the recent past, you can predict that there will be some muscle retribution afterward.

To reduce the chance of soreness under any long run mileage increase, don't run with the same form every step of the way. By taking walking breaks early and often you'll accomplish this.

"Why should I waste a race by running slowly?... I don't understand how you can run a slow race. You have to train for six months and I want to make the most of this once, or twice, a year challenge." I understand where you're coming from. For my first 60 marathons, I was the competitor. When the gun fired, the force of my being was directed at reaching the finish line as I would in any race: with nothing left. While I ran some fast times including a 2:16, I did not enjoy these experiences. When I placed well, such as a win at Honolulu and fifth and seventh place finishes at Boston, the afterglow was compromised by weeks of healing: soreness, tiredness, blisters and ego (which always told me, even when I ran well, that I could have run faster). By focusing on finishing and running with my wife Barbara, I have enjoyed every one of my last 70+ marathons... and look forward to many more.

110

To Run Faster...You Must Run Faster

*Y*ou can't run all of your runs slowly if you want to run fast in the race. But you can't go too fast either. By running the speed play too fast, for example, you will prepare your muscles to go out too fast in the race and pay dearly for that later. The best type of speed is that which simulates the race experience. This will encourage the exact type of endurance/speed adaptations necessary to go faster on race day.

Strength and coordination are developed simultaneously with the other improvements generated by speed sessions.

The cardiovascular system adapts:

• The heart pumps more blood into the exercising muscles.

• Waste products are withdrawn more quickly from those muscles.

Your oxygen processing system becomes more efficient:

• Oxygen is absorbed more efficiently from the air.

• Oxygen delivery to the muscles allows you to burn fat longer.

Adaptations occur inside the muscles due to the challenges of speed play:

• Fat-burning makes you more efficient.

• You also become more efficient when burning glycogen.

• Waste product removal gets more effective.

• Individual muscle cells work at a higher capacity for a longer period.

• Muscle cells learn to work together, in systems.

You develop the mental strength to go further:

• You develop instant and continuous mind-body feedback.

• You learn how to dig deeper and push through doubt.

• You learn the difference between real problems and the lazy messages of your left brain.

For more information on the changes in muscles, see Galloway's Book On Running, *pp. 24-33.*

But every time you run fast, you increase the chance of injury, you stress and fatigue the main running muscles, and you increase the chance that you'll not recover before the race itself. To do your best in your race, all of your components should be ready for top performance, working together and trained to make further adaptations under stress. The stress of speed play is necessary for you to run faster, but you need to monitor fatigue to avoid injury or overtraining.

RECOVERY! RECOVERY! RECOVERY!

The theme of a time-goal program is recovery. If you build enough rest into your program before you need it, your body will be continuously recovering, rebuilding and adapting for the performance demands of your goal. By preventing extra fatigue and taking extra rest even at the first hint of slower recovery, you can maintain a steady performance increase without taking a week or more off due to injury or overtraining.

MONITORING OVERSTRESS

Keep a log book next to your bed and write down your pulse rate before you get out of bed each morning. Do this before you've had a chance to think about anything stressful, like getting up, work, etc.

Why? When your exercising muscles are over-fatigued, they don't have the resiliency to help move the blood through the system in the smoothest way. The heart must work harder and registers this with a higher heart rate.

When to take a day off: After several weeks of listing your heart rate, you'll be able to tell what your lower baseline levels are. When you see a five percent increase over your low baseline, you should take an easy day. When the heart rate is 10 percent above baseline, just take the day off from running.

Recovery Enhancers

- Enough days off from running each week

- Long runs which are slow enough—with walk breaks

- Walking the rest interval between mile repeats

- Short walk breaks during mile repeats

- Starting out every run very slowly (at least three minutes per mile slower than you could run the distance you plan to run). You can speed up later in the run if everything is okay....just start very slowly. (Stay slow on long runs.)

- Making sure that you are recovered enough from the weekend sessions before you do any tempo running, accelerations, etc. during the maintenance runs on weekdays.

Note: An elevated heart rate may also indicate an infection. Talk to your doctor if you suspect this.

MILEAGE HELPS——BUT AT GREAT RISK

By adding mileage to your program, you'll improve overall conditioning and improve the chance that you can achieve your time goal. But higher mileage dramatically increases injury risk.

There are some ways to increase total mileage and reduce the chance of injury:

- By increasing mileage very gradually

- By adding a short additional run to a running day

How many days per week?

Almost every long distance runner, including most of those training for the Olympic Trials could benefit from more days off from running per week. Age will ultimately dictate how many more days off you will need. If you experience lingering fatigue, aches or pains:

- Those in their 30s can get by with two days off per week.

- In your 40s...better take three days off from running per week.

- If you're over 50, it's best to shift to every other day.

- Over 60, go to three days a week.

If you've been running six or seven days per week, I'd start by cutting back by one day per week. As the long runs reach 10 miles and beyond, cut one more day out of the schedule. You can actually increase mileage to running days by adding an additional run (if recovery is proceeding well). Alternative exercise can be done on non-running days, but take it very easy the day before:

- your long one,

- races and

- your speed play day.

Example: The late Dr. George Sheehan improved by reducing from six days to three days.

As he approached the age of 60, Dr. Sheehan's marathon times slowed down. For years, he had been running five miles a day, six days a week. Admitting that his competitive days appeared to be over, the running cardiologist cut back to three days a week, while increasing his daily mileage to 10 miles. In other words, weekly mileage held steady at 30 miles per week, while he gained three extra rest days.

After about three years of this schedule, at age 62, George ran the fastest marathon of his life: 3:01. He gained more training effect from one 10-miler than he did from two successive five-milers. Even more significant was the recovery he received by taking a day off between runs.

Note: See my book, Running Until You're 100, for much more information (www.JeffGalloway.com)

113

- By starting and finishing your running days with a mile each of very slow running (at least three minutes per mile slower than current 5K pace)

Be aware of all the early warning signs of injury or over-fatigue and back off at the first indication of trouble.

AS WE GET OLDER

Since it is possible to continue to improve times at any age, many runners over 45 are elated when they run personal records or high age-group performances...and forget that they're over 45. The exuberance of achievement may push race improvers at any age into over-fatigue before they know it; the older the runner, the longer he or she has to pay for the excessive training.

Unfortunately, there are few early warning signs of overtraining in a long distance program. Most of those who get into trouble are increasing gradually enough; they just don't have enough recovery time built into their program. The progessive buildup pushes the muscles beyond their limits so gradually that the effects are usually masked by internally produced stress hormones. Once the resource reserve has been used up, older runners must endure a long recovery period.

PAST THE AGE OF 35:

- Fatigue comes on more quickly but is usually masked by stress hormones.

- It's easier to push into overtraining without warning signs.

- The worse the overtraining, the longer the recovery.

Fatigue takes twice as long to recover from (compared to the below age 35 group).

Over-fatigue takes five to six times longer to recover from (compared to younger groups).

114 THE FATIGUE-PRODUCERS:

- too many days of running per week

- too many miles per week

- too many races

- speed sessions

- the very long, long runs run too fast

The volume of miles which most time goal racers put into their program is enough to produce overtraining among the over-35-year olds. It's so easy to push just a bit too hard on races, speed sessions or any of the other components, but the recovery from stepping over the line is significant.

REDUCING INJURIES FOR 35+

- Add an extra day off from running (to a minimum of three running days per week).

- Slow down long run to a pace of three minutes per mile slower than you could run that day.

- Add walk breaks to long runs, from the beginning.

- Walk for one to two extra minutes (minimum) during the rest interval in speed sessions.

- Carefully monitor resting heart rate.

LONG RUNS CAN IMPROVE SPEED

By increasing beyond 26 miles (beyond 13 miles for half), you'll build reserve endurance which will boost performance in many ways:

- You'll push your "wall" past 13/26 miles.

- You'll have the strength and stamina to maintain a hard pace during the last three to six miles when most competitive folks slow down.

- With reserve endurance, you can often get away with a few small pacing mistakes.

YOU MUST RUN SLOWLY OR YOU'LL LOSE THE BENEFITS:

- You get the same benefit from a long slow one as from a long fast one. You'll just recover faster from a long slow one.

- Going beyond 26 miles (13 for half) in the long one helps finishing stamina dramatically but you must run slowly. By pacing these long ones at least two minutes per mile slower than predicted by the "magic mile" *and* taking walking breaks, you'll get the job done!

- Running slower will help you recover faster and therefore keep the legs ready to do speed sessions on the following weekend.

- Liberal walk breaks will also speed recovery from the long ones. Remember that these one-minute walks must be taken early and often to give your legs the relief needed. (See the Run-Walk-Run chapter.)

- Make sure the maintenance runs during the week are done slowly enough. Sometimes a slight bit of fatigue will appear on the second or third day after a long one or a speed session. Take it very easy if that happens.

ACCELERATION-GLIDERS

To improve running form and efficiency, accelerations can help you greatly. When your form improves, a speed increase will occur naturally.

BENEFITS OF ACCELERATION-GLIDERS

- They warm up the legs before speed sessions, hills or races.

- By focusing on these gliders, you teach yourself efficient running form.

- They help you develop the capacity to glide or "coast" for segments of 50 to 200 meters, resting the major running muscles so that they will perform better later.

ACCELERATION-GLIDERS MUST BE DONE

- regularly—at least once a week

- with no sprinting—no major effort used

- low to the ground to minimize effort

- using quick turnover of the feet and legs

HOW TO DO THE ACCELERATION-GLIDERS

1. It helps to have a slight downhill to get momentum going, using the last 20 to 30 meters of the downhill as momentum to get right into gliding at an increased pace.

2. Keep the legs and body relaxed throughout but particularly at the beginning. Start by jogging for about 15 steps then fast jogging for about 15 steps.

3. If no downhill is available, pick up your leg rhythm by shortening stride length and gradually increasing the turnover of your feet and legs. (Turnover is simply the number of steps you take per minute.) Gradually increase over 15 steps or so.

4. You're now up to speed so just glide... keeping feet low to the ground, using very little effort.

5. Let this gliding continue for 20 to 40 steps. Gradually slow down.

6. Rest by jogging between accelerations. You may also take walking breaks as needed.

7. Start with two to three gliders and increase by one or two each session to a maximum of eight.

8. One of these sessions per week will help to mechanically reinforce form improvements, which will help you in the race itself.

9. You can use these as a warm-up before hills, speed sessions or races. You may also do them during your recovery/maintenance runs each week.

Note: My book, A Year Round Plan, *has these and other improvement drills inserted into a training schedule for each week (www.JeffGalloway.com).*

Hills Build Strength

*A*ll runners can benefit from doing some hill accelerations. Hill training provides a gentle and effective transition between very slow running and the faster speed play needed by veteran racers for faster performance. If you're just starting to run, you shouldn't jump into hill play. But those who've been running regularly for six months or more can benefit from the strength increase which only hill training can give. You don't have to have a time goal to benefit from play on the hills. *Note: Walkers can improve walking leg strength by walking up hills. Use a short stride.*

Hills: The Best Strength Training for Running

Hills provide resistance to the main running groups, primarily the calf muscles; the regular but gentle uphill stress encourages these muscles to develop strength in the act of running. Weight training, in contrast, builds static strength in only one range of motion at a time. Since weight work can strengthen some leg groups more than others (and knock your running motion off balance), it is not recommended for runners. Hill training strengthens as it coordinates the dynamic action of running

and can bestow all the running power you need. When runners of all ability levels run hill sessions regularly, they develop the lower leg strength to support body weight farther forward on their feet. As the foot rolls forward in the running motion, greater support strength will allow the ankle to be loaded like a strong spring. The result is a more dynamic lift-off of the foot as the ankle releases its mechanical energy. Due to the incredible efficiency of the ankle, more work is done with less energy expended by the muscles. Such conservation of muscle resources allows one to run further or faster or a combination of both.

If You're Doing Hill Training for the First Time...

Beginning hill runners should be conservative. It's too easy to run too fast in the first few sessions without realizing it. DON'T PUSH THE EFFORT! Run at a comfortable and non-fast pace on each incline during the first few hill sessions. The grade of the hill will be enough of a challenge to bestow a training effect. After three hill play sessions, you may run the hills a little faster.

Note: Hill sessions are integrated into the schedules in my book A Year Round Plan *(www.JeffGalloway.com).*

HILL TRAINING RULES:

* Never run all out!

* Never go to the point that you're huffing and puffing and can't talk.

* Don't run so hard that you feel significant tension or extreme exertion in any of the muscles or tendons in the back of your legs. If this happens, slow down immediately and shorten your stride. (The lengthening of the running stride out of its efficient range can cause injury, extra fatigue and long recovery.)

BENEFITS OF HILL TRAINING:

* Strength from hill training helps runners shift alignment farther forward on the foot and gain a more efficient "lift off" with each step.

* It strengthens a set of muscles which are used as back-ups for the main running muscles.

* It helps the cardiovascular system adapt to faster running without going into significant oxygen debt.

HILL TRAINING:

* Take a very slow one to two mile warm-up and warm-down.

* Pick a hill that is 50 to 300 steps long.

* The grade of the hill should be very gentle.

* Run up; walk down.

* Run with a smooth, continuous effort over the top of the hill.

* Never sprint or run all out. Just maintain an increased turnover rate over the top.

* Start with two or three hills, and increase by one or two hills per week until you can run eight hills.

* Don't feel like you have to increase the number each session. Back off if tired or sore.

HILL TRAINING FORM:

* Maintain upright body posture.

* Feet should stay low to the ground.

* Keep your stride short at first; pick up the rhythm until you feel comfortable.

* Keep your rhythm going quickly and smoothly over the top of the hill.

* If the muscles tighten during the hill, shorten stride to maintain turnover rate.

As in the other elements of training, it's important for hill sessions to be done regularly, in order to produce the adaptations desired from the legs and muscles and to improve overall running efficiency. Since hills will prepare the running muscles for a higher level of performance, the greater the number of weekly sessions, the more you will benefit from the added strength and running efficiency when you shift to speed play.

REMEMBER TO PUT THE PLAY IN HILL PLAY

By picking an interesting hill, you can improve your motivation and fun. You may vary the cadence or turnover of your legs in segments of the hill. When you have a hill play group, there is always the potential for more fun. (Just be sure that you aren't running faster than you should.)

117

HILL PLAY

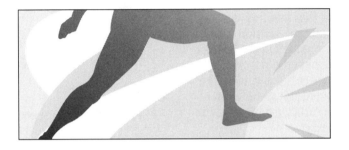

HILL PLAY SESSIONS

WHEN?

On non-long weekends, before speed play begins. During the early weeks of any program, two to four hills could be done in the middle of a Tuesday or Thursday run.

WARM-UP AND WARM-DOWN

A good walk of five minutes gets the blood flowing and the tendons and muscles warmed up. Start running very slowly, and jog for at least a half mile before doing any hills. The warm-down should reverse the warm-up. Runners and competitors could add 4 to 8 acceleration-gliders just before the hills and could increase the warm-up and warm-down to at least one mile.

HOW STEEP

The incline of the hill can increase to the maximums listed: one to two percent for both beginner groups, three to four percent for runners, and five to six percent for competitors. The grade is measured from horizontal being zero percent and perpendicular being 100 percent.

HILL PLAY ORGANIZATION

DEFINITIONS

Beginners have been running for less than three months and have never done any kind of speed play.

Advanced beginners have been running for more than three months but have never done speed play.

Runners have been running for more than six months and have done some speed play.

Competitors have been running for years and have done regular periods of speed play.

BEGINNER HILL PLAY

Grade: (1-2 percent) so easy that you barely feel the incline

Distance of hill segment: 50-100 walking steps long

Pace: about the same speed as your easy running on flat land (no huffing or puffing)

118

Hill Form

The resistance of the hill will strengthen the lower legs through repetition. Bouncing, high push-offs and long striding are counter-productive to hill form. Many runners aren't reminded about their form imperfections on the flat, but the extra effort required going up will aggravate form flaws. Your goal is to find the way of running which is easier, lighter on your feet, and which requires less effort. By increasing leg and foot turnover, you can often run faster while you run easier.

Run relaxed: Don't contract the muscles or strain to keep the right alignment.

Posture upright: Head is over shoulders, over hips, and all are lined up over the feet as they assume the weight of your body. Your alignment should be perpendicular to the horizontal and not the incline of the hill. In this way, you're most efficiently distributing the weight of your body as it interacts with gravity.

Short stride: Keep shortening the stride until you feel a slight relaxing of the hamstring muscles (back of thigh). If your stride is too short, you'll feel that you're slowing down due to choppy steps and loss of fluid motion. Too long a stride is noted by tightness in the hamstring and/ or the quadriceps muscle (front of thigh) and significantly more effort required for only a small increase in speed.

Feet low to ground: The less you have to lift your feet, the more effort you'll conserve.

Quick turnover: Those who want to improve speed and strength can gradually increase the cadence or turnover of legs and feet.

As the hill gets tougher: Keep reducing stride length, while trying to maintain or increase turnover of the legs and feet. Remember, stay light on your feet and keep feet low to the ground.

Recovery: walk slowly down the hill, and walk at the bottom for as long as needed

How many hills? Repeat the hill, as before: 2 to 3 hills on the first session, with an additional hill each week until you reach a comfortable number (maximum 8 hills).

ADVANCED BEGINNER HILL PLAY

Grade: (1-2 percent) easy so that you barely feel the incline

Distance of hill segment: 100-150 walking steps long

Pace: a little faster than the speed of your easy running on the flat, but no sprinting

Recovery: walk slowly down the hill and walk for 3-5 minutes at the bottom (more if needed)

How many hills? Repeat the hill, as before, starting with 2-3 hills and building to 8-10 hills.

119

RUNNER HILL PLAY

Grade: (3-4 percent)

Distance of hill segment: 200-300 walking steps

Pace: no faster than 10K race pace and usually slower

Recovery: walk slowly down the hill and walk for 3-5 minutes at the bottom

How many hills? Repeat the hill, as before, starting with 2-4 and building to 8 hills

COMPETITOR HILL PLAY

Grade: (4-6 percent) pick a grade which will allow you to maintain a steady speed and turnover over the top. If that means less of a grade, that's fine.

Distance of hill segment: 300-500 steps

Pace: about 10K race pace, adjust to maintain smoothness, relaxed leg muscles, and turnover

Recovery: jog and walk down the hill, walk for 2-3 minutes at the bottom

How many hills? Repeat the hill as before, starting with 3-4 and building to 8-10 hills.

Note: The distance range is longer in hill play for half or full marathons than that for shorter distance events. Make sure that you keep stride length short to maintain turnover without tension in leg muscles to avoid overexertion and to avoid extending your lower leg too far in front of you.

120

No competition!

Don't try to beat your workout partners during hill workouts. (Legs in varying stages of conditioning, which are not warmed up as they should be, can be pushed to injury when individuals try to stay with someone who is feeling good and in better condition than he/she is.)

LONGER HILLS FOR THE BOSTON QUALIFIER CANDIDATES

- Run longer hills
  - Run hills which are 30-50 percent longer than listed above

- Run the hills with no strong push off
  - Run smoothly but quick and light on the feet

- Start slowly and build into the quicker turnover

Q - Won't these longer hills keep you tired?

A - Not if you run them with the short stride indicated above. Through practice, you'd be amazed how fast you can turn your legs over when going uphill. By not overextending the hamstring or calf muscles, your legs feel reasonably fresh, even at the end of the session.

Q - How do you pick up the turnover?

A - Don't expect it to happen all at once. First, ensure that the hamstrings are loose and ready to respond to a quick turnover.

- The difference between the shortened stride and a stride which feels like it is giving full extension may be only an inch or so.

- You only need a slight stride shortening to relax the main running muscles.

- Relaxed muscles are more resilient, can respond quicker, and return to do it again quicker. This means quicker turnover.

Jeff Galloway:

Short uphill stride helped me run my fastest marathon...at age 35

The 1980 Houston-Tenneco course had several significant rolling sections, and this worried me. I had strained my hamstring eight weeks before the race and had to lay off from fast running. As the time closed in on the marathon date, I discovered that the only speed sessions I could do were hill repeats with a shortened stride. While the injury was not fully healed, I picked up the turnover and jokingly told myself that I was the fastest "short strider" in the U.S.!

The hill's resistance gave me the quality of speed play needed to run a high-performance marathon. The stride reduction released the tension on the hamstring and allowed it to continue healing. Not only did I recover while doing quality work, I passed about two dozen competitors while going up hills in the race itself. They were huffing and puffing, and I was zooming by at my normal respiration rate. I ran strong to the finish in a lifetime best of 2:16.

121

SPEED PLAY

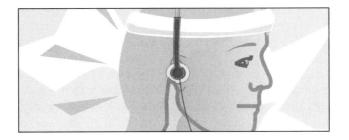

THE RIGHT TO HAVE FUN

Let me introduce you to a new type of speed session...one which offers the invigoration of going fast and the satisfaction of knowing you're getting better. You'll be able to joke with friends or yourself throughout the session and provide games which keep the experience interesting. Starting now, we have abolished the old, archaic speed work and replaced it with a clean, upbeat and uplifting speed play. You're going to like it so much that you'll finish each session wanting to do more. And because you don't do more than assigned, you'll look forward to the next session.

Set up your speed session in an interesting area. You can also change the venue if variety helps make it more interesting. Bring music, a clock (if possible) and banners which are funny, inspirational or instill pride. Some runners bring along a few posters with uplifting graphics. Many runners like to read something before the speed session. Humorous, entertaining, informative...any reading will offer the chance that the left brain will be preoccupied so that it won't bother you with negative messages and excuses.

Running with a group will improve morale, increase and maintain motivation and make the session more fun. The requirements of the group are as follows:

- You can start together but don't compete!

- Don't run the pace of someone who is faster than you.

- When in doubt, take more rest between repetitions, even if the rest of the group is not.

DO THINGS THAT ENSURE FUN

- Require each member to bring to each session 1) a joke, 2) a controversial viewpoint and 3) some spicy news.

- Set up games in which runners of all abilities can run the same repetition, with the winner being the one closer to his or her assigned pace.

- Alternate the jokes, etc. so that there is a continuous flow of entertainment.

- Use the walking between repetitions to share thoughts and support one another.

Note: There is a lot more information on speed training in A Year Round Plan *(www.JeffGalloway.com).*

WHERE

A track is not necessary. Road segments, a park, well-packed trails or other safe venues are just as good. Wherever you run, make sure that the mile or half mile segments are accurately measured. During the first few sessions, a track can help by giving regular timed feedback, usually every quarter mile. This helps to set the internal pace clocks more quickly. Also important is the ability to hear music as you make the loops of the oval. When choosing a road segment, avoid downhills that are too steep or give you too much advantage. Likewise, avoid uphills which are too steep and will force you to either slow down or overwork to maintain pace.

SPEED AND ENDURANCE

Running faster in the half or full marathon requires that you develop a special type of speed-endurance. This means that the actual pace of the speed segments is only slightly faster than goal pace. You're developing the capacity to maintain a moderate pace over a long distance. Compared with speed sessions for shorter distance racing goals, those for the half or full marathon emphasize building endurance by

* running longer repetitions

* increasing the number of repetitions to a maximum of 14

LEARNING HOW TO PACE YOURSELF

You'll gain a sense of pace at the same time you're developing the capacity to run mile after mile in the time you need. It's actually detrimental to run the repeats faster than your schedule prescribes (30 seconds faster than goal pace). If you exceed this speed limit, even in the beginning of the speed session, it becomes difficult for your internal pace clock to acquire the pace judgement

needed in the event itself. A fast start will either leave you struggling at the end of the session or produce tired muscles which require a long recovery.

RECOVERY, RECOVERY, RECOVERY!

Finally, the need for recovery cannot be overemphasized. Because the long runs and the speed sessions are long and fatiguing, everything possible should be done to speed up this important process.

* Strict adherence to the pace of the speed repetitions to avoid going too fast

* Lots of walking as rest between each mile repeat—when in doubt, walk some more (5 minutes between mile repeats, 3 minutes between half mile repeats)

* Enough easy days (and easy running) between the weekend sessions

HOW OFTEN?

To encourage the adaptations and improvements in form, rhythm, etc., speed sessions must be done regularly, that is, on most of the non-long weekends. (See Schedules.)

PICKING YOUR GOAL

The most important part of the speed development process is the very first step: picking a goal which is realistic for you. It's okay if your goal is slower than you are capable of currently running. This is a strategy which has led to many personal records. By setting yourself up for a performance that has some challenge but is realistic, you will take pressure off, stay in your right brain longer, and often achieve at a much higher level.

If your goal is too far ahead of your ability level, then you set yourself up for disappointment and fatigue. By overestimating your capacity, you'll force yourself to run

123

the speed sessions too fast. You just won't recover between speed days and long runs.

What a great reality check! If your "magic mile" performances don't predict the time you'd like, swallow your pride and select a less ambitious time goal. This means that you'll be slowing down the pace during the early part of the half or full marathon.

Always be conservative in choosing your goal. If the "magic mile" performances predict a 4:30 marathon, start the race at a 4:40 or 4:45 pace. It's always better to finish the race knowing that you could have run faster. Whatever you save in the beginning of the race will be available during the last 6 miles.

WARM-UP

Whatever speed play format you choose, get the blood flowing through the muscles in a gentle warm-up. This introduction to exercise allows the tendons, ligaments and muscles to warm up together and begin working as a team. A good warm-up will decrease the chance of injury and increase the intuitive cooperation of components within the muscles.

- Walk for three to five minutes.

- Use a more liberal walk ratio than you would normally use for six to eight minutes.

- Do four to eight acceleration-GLIDERS.

- Walk for three to five minutes.

STRETCHING

If you can't resist doing a gentle stretching routine before running, be very careful. Research has shown that stretching before running doesn't help you for that run, and it may increase your chance of injury. It's easy to overstretch a muscle that hasn't been engaged in much activity. This will leave the muscles tighter than before and more open to injury.

Don't make the most detrimental stretching mistake of trying to "loosen up" a tight muscle by stretching the heck out of it. A slow walk followed by very slow running and walking for six to eight minutes will allow the muscles to relax and warm up better than any stretch routine. Tight muscles tell you that you need to ease off on them until they feel loose.

On these days some runners require 3 to 5 miles of super easy walk-running to warm up. As we age, we need more slow warm-up distance at the beginning of every run. When it comes to the warm-up, slower is always better.

REPEAT MILE INTERVALS

The most popular form of speed play is that of "interval training," used by world-class athletes for most of the 20th century. In this format, measured segments (repetitions) are run at a pace that is slightly faster than half or full marathon goal pace, followed by a rest interval. This process is repeated many times.

Mile repetitions have worked better for the marathon and half mile (800 meter) repetitions for the half marathon and 10-miler.

LONGER REPETITIONS, SUCH AS THE MILE

- force your legs and feet to find more efficient ways of running, by eliminating or significantly reducing extraneous motions and getting the most efficient "lift-off" from each step

- develop better pace judgment, teaching you not to start races (and speed play) too fast

- help the internal systems to work together and become more efficient: muscles, pacing, intuitive connections and instinctive efficiency adjustments

- fine-tune the components of performance, such as energy sources to the muscle, waste removal, hidden resources to keep going, etc.

- develop the mental strength to continue running at a good pace even after fatigue sets in

- teach you when to keep going and when to stop to avoid damage

PACE OF SPEED SEGMENTS

Each mile should be run about 30 seconds faster than you want to run in the race itself, followed by a walk of a quarter mile (400 meters). Each 800 meter for the half marathon should be run 15 seconds faster than goal pace.

ADJUST FOR HEAT, HUMIDITY, ETC.

Even during the extreme heat of summer, you can continue doing speed sessions, but be careful. If you notice yourself or anyone in your group having symptoms of heat disease, stop the session and get medical attention immediately.

The best time of the day to do speed sessions on warm days is very early in the morning, before the sun rises. Be advised, however, that when the temperature is above 65-70 degrees, you should cut the distance of the repetition in half and walk more between each. (In this case, do twice as many repetitions.)

Note: When you feel that there is any possibility of heat disease or a cardiovascular problem, abandon the exercise, cool off and get help.

WALK BETWEEN EACH MILE REPEAT

It is better to walk between the repetitions to minimize fatigue and recovery. Most runners should walk 400 meters between each of the repeat miles and 300 meters between the 800-meter repeats. Walk more if you feel the need. The extra walking will not reduce the training effect of the speed session. If you have a heart rate monitor, keep walking until the heart rate goes below 65 percent of your maximum heart rate.

HOW MANY MILE REPEATS?

If you haven't done any speed play before, start with only one or two repeats. Veterans can begin with four to five repeats, and others can pick a starting number somewhere in between. On each session, increase the number of repetitions by one or two until you reach the upper limit for your respective goal listed on the time goal schedule.

PRACTICE GLIDING DURING EACH MILE

As you alternate between the prime running motion and your gliding motion, you'll save the muscles which do most of the work. The reduced demands of the gliding motion allow the main running muscles to regain a small amount of resiliency even as you are moving at a significant speed. By gliding early and often in speed sessions and in the race itself, you'll feel stronger at the end and will recover faster from each speed session.

Most importantly, you'll develop the teamwork between muscles which will bestow great performance benefit in the race itself.

The gliders should be a natural part of your running, but be sure to start them within the first 400 meters of each repetition. A glider of 50 to 100 meters, done about every 400 to 600 meters, is often enough to help you

125

integrate gliding into your racing routine at the same time that it helps you fine-tune your running technique. Be sure to go back and re-read the section on Acceleration-Gliders to reinforce the concept.

TROUBLESHOOTING SPEED SESSION PROBLEMS

Q: *I can't finish a speed session*—my legs just can't keep going at the pace needed. What's wrong?

A: If you're having trouble maintaining pace on the repeats, there are several possibilities:

1. Your goal is too ambitious for your current fitness level—adjust to slower repetitions.

2. You went out too fast in the first part of the speed session—slow down in the beginning.

3. Fatigue from other sessions is still there—you need more rest days or easier recovery days.

4. You need more rest between the repeats—double the walking between each.

Q: *I feel great on the speed work sessions* and have no trouble running them 40 seconds per mile faster than my goal pace, *but my legs don't 'have it' in the race itself*. Won't running the mile repeats faster help me run faster in the race?

A: No! You're actually hurting yourself by running faster than your assigned time (30 seconds faster than goal pace). The 30-second pace increase will develop the performance capacity and the pace judgement which has a proven record of success. The effort required to go faster than this can keep you tired for many days and compromise the other quality sessions in your program. Stick with the schedule for your best chance of success.

Q: *Between the repetitions, I've been jogging instead of walking* because I've heard that I'll get in better shape. Is this true?

A: No. By doing more walking between the hard repetitions, you won't lose any of the conditioning of that speed session. The extra rest during each repetition or speed segment will help the legs start recovering from that speed session while you're doing it. Walking between mile repeats (for the marathon) serves the same function as walk breaks during the long run: limiting muscle damage. If you've been running at the pace that you *should have* on the mile repeats, liberal walk breaks in mile repeat sessions will allow you to recover within a day or two in most cases.

PRACTICAL ADVICE

AGE ISSUES: ADJUSTMENTS AFTER 40

*"**I** feel better, at age 78, than I have felt in my 45 years of running. Slower, yes, but much happier with my exercising."*

I met a runner recently, after a 10-mile race, who was 93 years old. He was mentally alert and just as fired up about finishing as any of the other runners. The number of runners is growing, but the segment of those over 80 is growing faster. I'm proud to say that my father is one of them. These folks are clearly showing that the joys of running continue at any age if you're more conservative and use walk breaks.

The endorphins are the same at 80 as at 20. And the benefits of extra vitality and a positive attitude cannot be derived from any pills or any other activity I know. An 86-year-old man who ran 30 miles a week told me that his sedentary wife got on him constantly for not settling down and acting his age. He said the problem was mostly solved when he started running during her regular naps. His mileage actually increased and she didn't know any better.

NO BONE AND JOINT DAMAGE AFTER ABOUT 50 YEARS OF RUNNING!

Twenty-five years ago, many well-meaning doctors (who didn't run) told me that if I continued to run I could expect to be using a cane to walk by the time I reached the age of 55. I'm proud to say that I've passed that barrier now and am averaging over 30 miles a week, enjoying almost every run.

I'm actually part of a study. In the early 70s, the labs of David Costill, Ph.D. (physiologist) and Dr. Kenneth Cooper (Aerobics Institute founder) joined resources in a landmark study of world-class athletes. I was proud to be invited as a subject of this study. Over the past decade, these two labs have started bringing us back to see how much we've deteriorated. After doing bone scans, CAT scans, and X-rays of all major joint areas, I received a clean bill of orthopedic health.

My book *Running Until You're 100* has a chapter on the research showing that runners have healthier joints than non-runners.

If running could destroy joints and cartilage, I would have done it. During my competitive years, I pushed the edge, going over it into injury about every three weeks. I was so obsessed with performance that I continued to run, as hard as possible, until I could not. In dozens of cases, I had to take weeks or months off from running because I refused to take a day or two off at the first symptoms. Needless to say, I've had hundreds of injuries.

Fortunately, our bodies are programmed to adapt to running and walking and make adjustments. One X-ray specialist told me that I had the knees of a healthy 18-year-old. So now I want to pass on the adjustments I've made which not only have made running more enjoyable but also have kept me from having an overuse injury for almost 30 years.

VITALITY AND ATTITUDE

For a fit person, age is not often a factor. Sure, my muscles don't feel as good as they did even 10 years ago—but that doesn't matter, as long as I check my ego at the door as I leave the house. It was a wonderful revelation that slowing down allows you to feel great—just about every day. I'll also describe two other factors which speed recovery and make the exercise fun: running every other day and walk-breaks.

The quality of my life has been based upon two factors: vitality and attitude. Running maintains both at the highest possible level. For most exercisers over 50, attitude is often maintained at a lifetime best level. I believe that we become more introspective as we age. Running or walking provides a positive outlet for this continuous inward journey and more time to oneself to organize the brain and get things on track.

For runners and walkers over 50, fatigue is related to the number of training days per week and only indirectly the number of miles per week. For example, many of them have improved by taking an extra day or two off per week, while maintaining the same weekly mileage.

Our recovery rate slows down each year. By taking more days off, we speed up the rebuilding process. At the same time, a higher level of performance can often be achieved by increasing the number of miles run on an exercise day. Speed and endurance sessions which are specifically designed for the half or full marathon, for example, have allowed many runners and walkers to improve as they have pushed up to the next age group.

ALTERNATIVE EXERCISE

On non-training days, an alternative exercise will boost performance without pounding. The exertions which produce the most direct improvement are water running and cross-country ski machine exercise. Walking, rowing and bicycle sessions are great for recovery and bestow some indirect benefits. Swimming and weight training help to balance the muscle development of the body but don't help to improve your running. Stair machines, high impact aerobics and leg strength exercises are not recommended and can slow down the recovery process.

How Many Days Off Per Week?

Those who are having aches, extra fatigue, etc. can cut back the number of training days to the following:

40 year-old long distance runners and walkers need three days off from running.

Over 50-year-old long distance runners and walkers should shift to every other day running or walking.

Over-60 folks should run or walk three days per week and monitor for fatigue.

The over-70 crowd can maintain a significant level of performance by training two days a week and taking an endurance walk or water running session as a third workout each week.

129

Performance Tips for the Over-40 Crowd: getting better as you get older

Workout twice a day on the workout days:

Usually the first workout is very slow.

Accelerations or hills can be done on the second one—but be careful.

Accelerations maintain a high leg turnover:

Runners in their 50s can do accelerations on each of the afternoon workouts.

Runners in their 60s can do accelerations twice a week on the afternoon workouts.

Runners in their 70s can do accelerations once a week on an afternoon workout.

Remember that accelerations are merely increased turnover drills and not sprints. If your legs are tired or too tight, don't do the accelerations.

Long Training Session Pace: Three minutes per mile slower than you could go that distance on that day.

Yes, this is a minute slower than younger exercisers would go, but it will give you the same endurance, based upon the mileage covered. Remember to account for heat, humidity, hills, and other factors as you set your pace. I start my long runs about four minutes per mile slower than I could race the distance, and I not only feel great at the end of the run, but in two or three days, I'm almost always recovered, even from a 26-miler. I know, I can see the looks on some of your competitive faces. Yes, it will take a longer time to cover these long ones, but this just gives you more time to brag about your grandchildren. In our training groups, grandparents have a priceless opportunity: a captive audience for several hours!

Increase the length of the long training session beyond race distance:

The purpose of the long one is to build endurance only. The slower you go, the quicker you'll recover. By having at least one long one beyond 13 or 26 miles, you can boost your endurance limit, which will allow you to maintain a hard race pace for a longer time in the event itself. When you go the extra distance, it is crucial to take the breaks and adhere to the pacing guidelines. For maximum performance, the longest workout should be 15-17 miles for the half and 29-30 miles for the marathon. Again, you must go extra slowly on these extra long ones and take frequent breaks. *(See Run-Walk-Run chapter in this book.)*

Alternate long runs with other weekend runs:

Until the long one 17 miles, you may do it every other weekend. After that point, go long every third weekend. When the long one reaches 26 miles, you have the option of taking four weeks between. On non-long weekends, follow this time goal schedule.

Accelerations:

Keep your feet low to the ground—stride short. While staying light on your feet, pick up the rhythm after about 100 to 150 meters, glide by reducing the effort while maintaining the turnover.

Age Magnifies The Damage

Even young athletes will suffer from the following mistakes. Because recovery rate slows down each year, the negative effects of "stepping over the line" are more dramatic and long-lasting in those of us who are... challenged by age.

Junk miles

Going a few miles on a day when you could be resting keeps the muscles from fully recovering. You're better off not going at all on an easy day and adding those miles to a running or walking day—either as part of an extra warm-up or warm-down or as a separate session.

Starting too fast

Whether on a slow training session or in a race, a pace that is too fast in the beginning will cause a slowdown at the end and/or damage to the muscles, requiring a longer recovery time. It is always better to start out at a slower pace than you think you can maintain. Practically all personal bests among my "over 50" clients are accomplished with a negative split: the second half faster than the first.

Overstride

When runner and walkerss of all ages err on the length of their stride, they tend to overstride. The negative consequences are greater for those over 50 in terms of tendon and muscle damage and the recovery time required for healing. Runners are most likely to overstride when tired at the end of long runs, races or speed sessions. To avoid this problem, work on a lighter step with a shorter stride. The primary sensation is a lowering of tension in the hamstring muscle.

Overstretching

When there is tension in the running and walking muscles, many exercisers mistakenly try to "stretch it out." Massage is a better treatment mode in this situation. But there's hope. When you feel that you've overdone it, don't stretch the area for an extended period of time, talk to a therapist about massage, and ask your doctor if antiinflammatory medication is okay.

As in the other situations mentioned above, the damage takes longer to heal when you're past the age of 50. The best strategy is, as always, prevention.

Overexertion in speed or hill sessions

Young or old, every runner and walker pushes too far when doing higher performance sessions.

Again, it is the older runners and walkers who have to pay dearly with a longer "down" time when this happens. Be particularly careful when going faster than in the recent past.

When increasing the number of speed or hill repetitions, do so very gradually. By taking more rest between repetitions, you'll reduce the chance of overuse injury and speed up the recovery time after each session. When doing a repeat mile session, for example, 40-year-old marathoners should take at least a 400 meter walk between miles. Fifty-year-olds need at least an 800 meter walk between, 60-year-olds should use 1200 repeats (walking 800 meters), and those over-70 folks should use 800 meter repeats, walking 800 meters in between.

Recommended number of running/walking days per week by age:

Note: When runners and walkers have aches and pains (or injuries), the following schedule has helped to allow the body to recover. If you are running or walking more days than this per week and are not having problems, I see no reason why you cannot continue.

(You can walk or cross train on 2-3 other days if desired.)

35 and under: no more than 5 days a week

36-45: no more than 4 days a week

46-59: every other day

60+: 3 days a week

70+: 2 longer run days and 1 walk day

80+: One longer run/walk, one shorter run/walk and one very easy short walk

Note: The day before the long run should be a day of rest.

More walk breaks

The simple addition of more walk breaks, from the beginning of exercise, has allowed many mature runners to maintain mileage while reducing aches and pains.

Adjustments for Runners

132

Pace per mile	Run Amount	Walk Amount
7:00	4 minutes	20 seconds
7:30	4 minutes	25 seconds
8:00	4 minutes	30 seconds
8:30	3 minutes	30 seconds
9:00	2 minutes	30 seconds
9:30	2 minutes	40 seconds
10:00-11:30	1.5 minutes	30 seconds
11:30-13:30	1 minute	30 seconds
13:30-14:59	30 seconds	30 seconds (or 1-1)
15:00-17:00	30 seconds	45 seconds
17:00-20:00	20-30 seconds	1 minute

A longer and easier warmup

As the years go by, it takes longer (during an individual run or walk) for the legs to feel good. Here is what I recommend:

- At least 5 minutes of very gentle walking

- Then 5 minutes of walking at varied paces. Even if you walk a bit faster during the second 5 minutes, use a short stride.

- Runners will then insert some run breaks into their walk for 10 minutes. Start with 10-20 seconds of running followed by a minute of walking, then gradually shift to a minute of running and a minute of walking—or 30 sec/30 sec. Walkers will then settle into their walk/shuffle ratio for the day.

- Runners should then ease into the running pace and the run-walk-run frequency for that day.

- It is always better to be conservative— walk or shuffle more frequently if needed.

Breaking up your daily mileage into 2 or 3 sessions

A runner recently told me that her fitness improved during the year after she retired from her career in nursing. Instead of walking her 3 miles once a day, she walked 2 miles in the morning and 2-3 miles in the afternoon. She enjoyed the vitality boost from both sessions.

My favorite marathon companion

Before I started running, I had been a fat and inactive kid. Like many boys, I wanted to be like my Dad. In the eighth grade, I tried the sport in which he had achieved "all state" status: football. At first I sensed that my temperament wasn't quite right for the sport ("Hit 'em harder, Galloway. Make 'em feel your impact."). By the end of that season, I knew that my temperament wasn't right for that sport that was supposed to "make a man of you."

My dad steered me into cross country, where I felt instantly at home. I'm only guessing, but any parent would tend to want his or her child to hang out with the type of kids that choose to run distance events. Then, as today, at just about any high school, these athletes are better students and leaders of many school activities. I found them to be interesting and fun to run with. When my progress seemed to stagnate, my dad brought me some reading material about various training programs, including those of the great New Zealand coach Arthur Lydiard. These readings gave me the principles which I use to this day.

As I moved on to college, I became more fit as my sedentary Dad increased his fat. By my mid-20s, continuing to read about fitness, I became concerned about my father's health as he tipped the scales above 200 pounds. Not aware of the way our health is influenced by such factors, he complained about aches and pains and displayed an increasingly more negative attitude in general. He read the book Aerobics and other readings I gave him, but his sedentary behavior didn't change. On one occasion, when I suggested walking around the park in front of his office, he explained how his varicose veins and allergies prevented him from exercising. I stopped arguing with him.

A high school reunion, at the age of 52, changed his life. At this gathering of the Moultrie, Georgia class of '37, it was discovered that out of 25 boys who had been on the football team from that class, 13 had died of lifestyle, degenerative diseases. Out of all the activities of the weekend, this fact weighed on his mind on the three and a half hour ride back. By the time he turned into his driveway, Elliott Galloway realized that he could be the next one to drop from the roster, and he was determined to do something about this. Starting at a particular telephone pole he set off that first day, determined to run the threemile loop across the street from his office. Reality was harsh. He had to settle for only the next telephone pole, about 100 meters away. On each successive run, the goal was one additional pole, until he made it completely around. Almost two years later he was running 10K races. Seven years later, and 55 pounds lighter, he was running marathons, including one below the three-hour mark. Having had an irregular heart rhythm for years, he decided, upon receiving doctor's orders, to finish his marathon career in 1996 at the 100th running of the Boston Marathon. He consented to letting me tag along with him. It would be my 100th marathon finish and the one I will remember for the rest of my life.

As we started, the thought hit me that the Boston Marathon had only been run 23 times when my Dad was born. I forced him to walk at each mile mark—as best I could. You see, he doesn't listen to what I say. I had run Boston four other times, trying to do my best time in each. As we shared the scenery, the energetic crowd and the landmarks, I hardly remembered any of it. Oxygen debt must erase your memory cells. This was a day for savoring, and we did.

As we turned the corner and saw the finish structure, my Dad took off. We were zooming down the final straight as the clock ticked away towards a time barrier which we were determined to break: six hours. We did: 5:59:48. He told anyone who asked about the race that he would have run much faster if I hadn't slowed him down.

Now that I've pushed past the 50-year barrier, my Dad is my hero again. I hope I can be like him when I grow up.

133

ACHES, PAINS AND INJURIES

*By taking a day or two off, at
the first sign of an injury, you can avoid two to
three weeks, or months, off later.*

*Most injuries come from going too fast
on long training sessions and not taking breaks.*

WEAK LINKS

Everyone has them. Each of us, due to unique biomechanics and structured patterns of motion, tend to aggravate specific areas over and over. When we exercise too many days per week or increase intensity or mileage too rapidly, these sites are usually the first to be aggravated. This is an early warning signal to back off before we push into injury. Half or full marathon training is more likely to reveal the weak links than most forms of exercise.

MOST COMMON SITES OF WEAK LINKS

1. Knee
2. Foot
3. Achilles tendon
4. Ankle

BE AWARE OF AREAS WHICH

- get sore first
- are repeatedly sore, painful or inflamed
- take longer to warm up
- have been sites of injury before
- are not functioning in their usual way

As you become more sensitive to these areas, you'll take time off for recovery and treatment at the earliest of warning signs. Quick and early action will cut down on the chance that you'll have to spend weeks or months of recovery later.

IS IT AN INJURY? WHAT ARE THE SIGNS?

- Inflammation: look for swelling around the injury site
- Loss of function: the muscle, foot, tendon, etc. doesn't work the way it should
- Extended pain which increases or hurts consistently for a week or more

INFLAMMATION

This is the body's attempt to immobilize an injured area to keep you from damaging the injury further. The excess fluid around the injury notifies you that there is a problem in the weak link. Your range of motion is thereby reduced, which normally limits the extent of further damage to the area.

External swelling is usually apparent, such as the swollen area around a sprained ankle.

Internal inflammation is harder to spot. At joints, tendon connections, and in small areas of muscle, it only takes a little bit of inner swelling to reduce the capacity of the muscle and produce pain. Be very sensitive to the possible minor muscle (or tendon) pulls or strains in areas such as behind the knee, at the insertion between hamstring and butt muscle, the adductors, the abductors and the lower back muscles.

Repair and rebuilding of the muscle will be speeded up dramatically as you reduce or eliminate the inflammation around the injury.

LOSS OF FUNCTION

If the tendon, muscle or other injured part is not doing its job, then several negative forces can be working against you. By ignoring it and continuing to run or walk, you're very likely to injure it further. If you take a day or two off from running or walking at the beginning of an functional injury, you may avoid having to take weeks or months off later due to abusing it.

Running or walking with an injury can produce a new injury by compensation. When the muscle, tendon, etc. doesn't function to capacity, the workload of running or walking shifts to other components which are not designed to handle the stress. In many cases, this produces a series of "compensation" injuries.

PAIN THAT DOESN'T GO AWAY

Temporary aches and pains will come and go throughout a long distance training program. These will usually be gone after a day or so, indicating that you probably don't have a serious injury. But if you sense an increase in pain or the pain continues for five to seven days, you should treat it as an injury (at least two days off from running or walking, ice and other treatments as necessary). Continued pain, even without loss of function, can be an early sign of internal inflammation.

DON'T TRY TO "STRETCH OUT" A TIGHT MUSCLE!

It's a mistake to push a muscle to its stretch limits when it feels tight or is fatigued. Stretching is actually the third leading cause of injury because well-meaning runners stretch when inflammation gives the sensation of tightness. Muscles which are tight during exercise can benefit from massage, walking and a shortening of the stride length—but not stretching.

The fatigue of long workouts and speed sessions will tighten the muscles and reduce strength and range of motion. Stretching fatigued muscles will not improve their performance. It will tear the fatigued fibers, producing injury and increasing recovery time.

Don't be fooled if at first the extra stretching makes the muscles feel good. This is probably due to the endorphins released to kill the pain of the many little "rips" in the muscle or tendon caused by stretching a fatigued muscle.

You're almost certain to overstretch a tired muscle and engage the stretch reflex. This protective mechanism tightens the muscle up in order to protect it. Even while the endorphins are telling you that the muscle is feeling great, you may be tearing them into a serious injury. At the end of long ones or speed sessions, fatigue will loosen the con-

135

Moral: Stretching when you're fatigued will often lead to some kind of stretching injury.

nections, allowing you to easily stretch the muscles into an overextended position.

ANTI-INFLAMMATORY MEDICATIONS CAN HELP, BUT ASK YOUR DOCTOR!

Many runners and walkers have reported that taking anti-inflammatory medications (ibuprofen, etc.) immediately after a difficult workout can significantly reduce the chance of inflammation and injury and speed healing. Be sure to talk to your doctor, even before taking over-the-counter medications because all have some side effects. Taking any medication before or during a long training session or race is not recommended. Whenever taking medications, follow the advice of your doctor and the instructions on the medicine and discontinue their use at the first sign of potential problems.

INJURIES: HOW TO TREAT THEM

* **Get a doctor** who knows running and walking and stay in touch with him or her. Getting a good diagnosis can speed the treatment and get you back on the roads quicker. A good doctor's advice and treatment can speed recovery by several weeks. It can often mean the difference between whether you will get to the starting line of your event or not next year.

* **Don't stretch** the area until it heals (unless you've injured the I-T band—ask your doctor).

* **Stop activity** that could possibly use the injured site for at least one to two days. In most cases your doctor will tell you that the injury doesn't have to heal completely before you go out again, but you must get the healing started and continue a program that doesn't re-injure it. Again, talk to the Doc.

* **Ice!** If the injury site is near the surface of the body, ice massage will usually help. Be sure to use a chunk of ice and rub it directly on the injured area until it is numb (usually about 15 minutes). This is particularly helpful for all tendon and other foot injuries. Be sure to ice at the first sign of injury, ice as soon as possible after exercise, and keep icing for at least a week after the pain goes away. The regularity of the ice treatment is very important so do it every day! In deeper tendon or muscle injuries, ice treatment may not have any effect but should cause no harm. Ice bags and gel ice do no good in my opinion.

* **Compression** will help to restrain further inflammation. Wrapping a sprained ankle soon after injury will reduce the inflamation. This is another area where your running/walking-oriented physician should advise you. (You must release compression regularly.)

* **Elevation** can help to reduce inflammation. An injured leg, for example, would be elevated on a pillow or two as you read or watch TV in bed.

* **Massage** can dramatically speed up the healing of muscle injuries. A massage therapist or physical therapist, who is experienced in working with runners, should be able to advise you 1) whether your injury will heal quicker with massage and 2) when it's time to work on it (immediately after injury is not usually a good time).

GETTING BACK OUT THERE

* If the short (one to two day) layoff from training allowed the healing to start, then an easy run or walk on the injured area is usually okay, if it's not causing further

injury. Exercise no more often than every other day and listen to the advice of an experienced doctor who knows running and walking injuries.

• **Choose alternative exercise** which will not aggravate the injured area and ease into it.

• **Continue with your injury treatment** as advised by the doctor. (Ice for at least one week after all symptoms go away.)

• **Gradually ease back** into your normal exercise routine as the healing takes hold.

For more information on injuries, see Galloway's Book On Running, *pp. 191-222* *www.JeffGalloway.com.*

137

THE COMEBACK:
STARTING BACK AFTER INJURY, SICKNESS, VACATION, ETC.

*D*o you have to start all over if your training program is interrupted? Probably not. Most of us are not in a position to quit our job, leave our family and other responsibilities to train for a long distance event and must steer our aerobic ship around the obstructions. There are as many ways to rebuild from a layoff as there are problems which cause the interruptions.

INJURIES

- At the first sign of an aggravated "weak link," take an extra day or two off.

- If it's an injury, see a doctor and get treatment immediately: the sooner treated, the sooner healed.

- Start alternative exercise immediately: the sooner started, the more fitness retained. (Water running is best.)

COMING BACK FROM AN INJURY

- Make sure the healing is continuing as you get back into running or walking routine.

- Stay in touch with your doctor or physical therapist to limit the risk of reinjury.

- Continue to treat the injury as prescribed by the doctor.

- Ice massage, for example, should be continued every day for two weeks after the disappearance of all symptoms in an Achilles tendon injury.

SICKNESS

- If Doc allows you to do some low level exercise (30 min, 3 x a week), do it!

- Always avoid the chance of lowering resistance to disease and getting sick again.

- Return to exercising conservatively after sickness.

- Don't run or walk if you have a lung infection.

TRAINING INTERRUPTIONS OF LESS THAN 14 DAYS DUE TO BUSINESS, TRAVEL, VACATION, ETC.

- You can come back to your normal weekly mileage in two to three weeks.

- But every session must be done slowly: follow the "two-minute rule."

BRING BACK THE LONG ONE

- You may increase the length more rapidly than usual by slowing down and taking more breaks.

- The longer your layoff from exercise, the more conservative your "comeback."

YOUR FIRST LONG ONE ON THE "COMEBACK TRAIL"

For your first long session after a layoff from exercise, start from your longest distance, three weeks before the day you plan to re-start the long ones and

- take off 20 percent per week if you did no exercise at all,

- take off 10 percent per week if you did 30 minutes of alternative exercise, three times a week, or

- take off five percent per week if you did alternative exercise which simulated marathon schedule.

For example, a runner named Chris ran 23 miles three weeks ago (4-1 ratio). Three days after that, he ran too hard on the mile repeats and injured his Achilles tendon. He did no running for three weeks, then he ran easy every other day for 10 days.

Today his Achilles felt secure enough for a long one. He would have had the following options, in terms of long run distances:

- a four to five mile long run, if he had done no exercise at all during the layoff,

- 10 to 13 miles if he did 30 minutes of alternative exercise three times a week, or

- 15 to 17 miles if he did alternative exercise which simulated his marathon schedule.

Chris had either run in the water or exerted himself on the XC ski machine about every other day but for mostly minimal amounts. He decided that 15 miles would be his target for his first restarted long one (2-1).

HOW DO YOU PACE THE LONG ONES WHEN YOU START BACK?

- The first two miles should be three to four minutes per mile slower than you could run that distance.

- You could settle into a pace that is three minutes per mile slower or maintain original pace.

- Take breaks twice as often.

HOW QUICKLY CAN YOU INCREASE THE LENGTH OF THE LONG ONE—AND GET BACK INTO "HALF OR FULL MARATHON RANGE"?

- Four to five miles per long session: when going more than three minutes per mile slower than you could go

  - and taking breaks twice as long and twice as often as before the interruption

- Three miles per long session: when going two and a half to three minutes per mile slower than you could go

  - and taking breaks twice as often as before the interruption

- Two miles per long session: when going two minutes per mile slower than you could go

  - and taking walk breaks as often as before the interruption

THE BEST SHOE

***The best advice in choosing a running or walking
shoe is to get the best advice . . .
at an authentic running or walking specialty store.***

*M*ost runners and walkers collect a closet full of bargain shoes until they find a real running or walking specialty store. The good advice of a trained staff can cut through the conflicting information, match you up with current helpful technology and help you find a shoe that becomes an extension of your foot.

Except for computer components and internet software, and, of course, the latest in women's fashion, there are few areas in life that change as rapidly as running/walking shoes. A tiny portion is fueled by new technology. Unfortunately, most of the flux is generated by the sales hype of companies competing to get on the feet of a growing army of new and addicted runners and walkers.

For efficiency, you need an expert at a true specialty store. While rare, the authentic running and walking stores are managed and staffed by adult runners/walkers who make it their life to test shoes, learn about the action of the foot and collect continuous feedback on what shoes really work.

That's why I opened my running store, Phidippides, in 1973. I still own the store but my other activities keep me away most of the time. So now, I consult my staff each time I need a new pair of shoes. They

The Top Five Reasons Why You Need Shoe Advice

1. Even the better shoe companies are using gimmicks in their design: some of the gimmicks work, and some don't.

2. There's always a reason why the catalog offers a dramatic discount on a given shoe.

3. The same shoe may be made in different factories—making each significantly different in the way it fits and in the many subtle ways it works when you run or walk.

4. Only people who are really into running or walking shoes can keep up with the gossip on them—due to constant feedback they receive from hundreds of customers each week who really use the shoe for exercise.

5. Only experienced staff people can look at you running or walking in a shoe and help you tell whether it really fits—and works with your foot in the right way.

haven't been wrong yet! If you're in Atlanta, please drop by.

IF YOU CAN'T FIND A RUNNING SPECIALTY STORE...

The following procedure will help you sift through the maze of running shoes. If you follow the steps below and use your best instincts, you're more likely to choose a shoe that will work for you. You'll also save time instead of listening to the pitch of commission-driven sales people or high school kids, at stores that sell all types of sport shoes.

BRING WITH YOU: YOUR WORN SHOES, THE SOCKS YOU USE, FOOT DEVICES, ETC.

You need to bring to the fitting process everything you would use on a workout. If you forgot to bring the socks that you use, buy a pair in the store that closely matches the thickness of your favorite ones. A good shoe expert can "read" the wear pattern on your shoes, which is the best indicator of how your foot functions. If you don't have this resource available, look at the diagram on the next page.

YOU'RE IN CHARGE

Sure, you want the best advice available. But you are the only one who can feel how the shoe works on your foot. Narrow down the selection and then run in each shoe. Finally, you'll decide which works best for you as you train. Don't let anyone tell you that a specific shoe is the shoe for you if another shoe seems to feel better or feels more natural on your foot. Get the best advice and then make up your mind.

BE PREPARED TO SPEND A LITTLE TIME

By spending at least 45 minutes (if you need it), you'll be more likely to try out the various shoe choices. Rushing in and grabbing the same shoe you got last year usually doesn't work at all. There are often production changes with all shoes within a four-month period so the same shoe isn't the same shoe. Besides, it's very likely that you'll find a better one for your needs. Try out all of the options and then decide for yourself.

TELL YOUR SHOE EXPERT...

In case you get a good staff person, be prepared to tell the following: the terrain of your routes, your training schedule, injuries (particularly chronic ones), goals in the next six months, etc. The staff person should ask you about those items, but if this doesn't happen, tell him or her.

TRY OUT IN EACH SHOE

Ask the salesperson to define the word "over-pronation." If they pass the test, ask him or her to watch you run or walk in each shoe. As you feel how each one works, get feedback from your expert. While the input is beneficial from knowledgeable staff persons, you are still the person who will make the decision.

FIRST, LOOK AT FUNCTION AND THEN GO FOR FIT

Once you've found two to three shoes (at least) that seem to function well on your foot (rigid, floppy), adjust the lacing to fine-tune the fit of the shoe.

BOTTOM LINE: WHICH WORKS BEST?

Look carefully at the two crucial factors listed immediately below. As you run or walk in each one of your final candidates, determine which one fits your foot naturally and functions as an extension of your foot. If both shoes seem to be equal, ask the shoe expert which one lasts longer and whether the store has any customer feedback about how well they work a month or two down the road.

The DON'Ts of shoe selection

1. Don't get a shoe because it has worked well for someone else.

2. Don't select the shoe that best matches your outfit.

3. Don't take too seriously the advice of someone who can't give you a good definition of "over-pronation."

4. Don't buy from a shoe store that won't let you run or walk in the shoe before purchase.

5. Don't pick the first shoe offered—especially if the salesperson says "Trust me, I know that's the best shoe for you."

6. Don't buy from a store where the average age of the staff is less than voting age.

7. Don't buy from a salesperson who tells you about his or her training, best times, etc. and doesn't ask you about your foot problems, past shoe successes and special needs.

8. Don't buy a shoe only because it's the most expensive.

DEFINITIONS: PRONATION, OVER-PRONATION AND SUPINATION

Pronation is the normal rolling in of the foot to a flat or neutral position as you walk or run to absorb shock. Most of us land on the outside of the heel and roll quickly to the forefoot. Your foot pronates, or rolls inward, to a flat and stable position before rolling forward off the toe.

Over-pronation is rolling beyond the flat or neutral position of the foot to the inside, which can produce injury (but not always).

Due primarily to the structure of leg and foot bones and tendons, the foot continues to roll to the inside as you push off. This usually over-rotates the knee but can also cause damage to the hip, shin, ankle and forefoot. When the force of your body weight presses down on a support structure that is out of alignment (as is the case with over-pronation), the weak link in your body will become injured. If there is any wear on the inside of the forefoot, you are an over-pronator.

Supination is rolling to the outside of the foot, which is usually okay because the bones on the outside of the foot are designed to support body weight. This motion may cause a problem when the foot continues to roll outside excessively, stressing the tendons of the ankle and sometimes the outside of the knee. The over-supination motion is noted by excessive shoe wear on the outside of the shoe and little wear elsewhere.

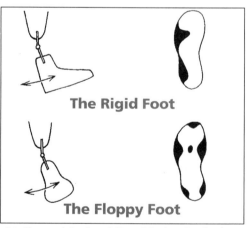

The Rigid Foot

The Floppy Foot

printed by permission from Galloway's Book on Running *from Shelter Publications, p. 247.*

FUNCTION: ARE YOU FLOPPY OR RIGID?

Imagine that your foot has hinges, like a door. The floppy foot is hinged so that the foot rolls easily from side to side. In contrast, the rigid foot moves forward and back.

Floppy feet often strike the ground first on the outside of the heel but roll to the inside as the body moves forward. This type of foot usually shows wear in spots, including some that are on the inside of the forefoot.

Rigid feet tend to push off strongly forward on the ball of the foot, showing wear on the outside of the forefoot, as well as the middle. Sometimes runners/walkers have one foot that's floppy and one that's rigid. Whatever type of foot you seem to have, there's no need to worry if you're not having aches, pains or injuries. Most feet make adaptations so that runners/walkers don't get injured due to their specific motion pattern. Increased stress due to mileage increase, speed training or not enough days per week off can all tip the scales toward injury.

Runners and walkers with floppy feet that get injured should try a stable shoe, one that provides the foot with a good platform (this usually means minimal cushion in the forefoot). There are shoes specifically designed for motion control and orthotic and other foot devices that reduce the chance of excessive rolling to the inside as the foot pushes off. Talk to a doctor before putting anything in your shoe. Orthotics can often help over-pronators who have chronic problems due to alignment. Soft shoes can compromise a foot support system.

SHAPE: ARE YOU CURVED OR STRAIGHT?

The "last" is the mold around which the shoe is built. If you look at a curved lasted shoe from the bottom of the sole, not only does it have a noticeable indention on the inside middle of the arch, but it actually curves so that the forefoot is supported more on the inside. When you look at a straight last shoe, however, the left shoe looks very similar to the right. Actually,

most of the shoes today are mixtures of a curved and a straight last.

If a shoe puts pressure on the outside of your foot and there's extra room on the inside, you are trying on a shoe that is too curved for your foot. Ask to see a straighter one. But if a shoe seems to put pressure on your big toe and joint, you need a shoe that is more curved.

Your foot should feel comfortable, naturally surrounded and protected—but not pushed up or pressured. The support of the shoe should be offered naturally so that you barely feel it. Never buy a shoe if it pinches or rubs parts of your feet when running. You know you've got a great fit when you try out the shoe and don't feel the shoe at all. Don't expect to get this perfect fit every time.

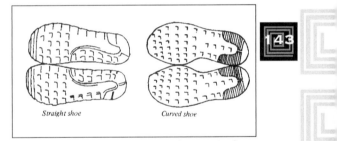

Straight shoe   Curved shoe

printed by permission from Galloway's Book on Running from Shelter Publications, p. 248.

BE SURE TO LACE YOUR SHOE SECURELY AROUND THE ANKLE

Many runners/walkers don't pull the laces tight when they try on a shoe. A loose fit at the ankle mistakenly seems to have an ill-fitting heel. If there is excessive heel motion, pull the last few laces snug and tie the lace together so that there is not a gap right at the knot. This may take several attempts because a new nylon lace is slick and resists being tightly knotted.

DON'T GET LOCKED INTO SPECIFIC MODELS OR BRANDS

After trying on one or two shoes of a brand that didn't fit, some people assume that all of the shoes of that brand, until eternity, are made the same way. All major brands have various lasts and shapes, which can fit most runners and walkers, and they introduce a new batch about every six months. Be open to the suggestions of your shoe expert, if you have one available, who will sort through the hundreds of models currently available to find the best match for your foot. (Ask about the magic word "overpronation.")

WHEN TO BUY ANOTHER SHOE

As soon as you know that a shoe fits and feels good when training, get an identical pair ASAP before the company discontinues it. Each week, at the end of a training ses-

sion, break out the new pair and go around the block. Over the weeks, you'll break in the new pair. But this is also a reality check on shoe support of the original pair. After a month or so, you'll know when the original shoe needs to move on to greener pastures—as a lawn-mowing shoe. On that day, the new shoe gives support, while the old one flips, flops and wobbles.

Note: for more information, see Galloway's Book on Running, *pp 244-254.*

Note: Your legs and feet make adaptations to the running/walking motion over months and years. It's possible for some over-pronators to avoid aches and pains through this process. If you over-pronate but are not having problems, it's not a great idea to get a corrective shoe. Stay with the type of shoe that has worked for you.

RUNNING FORM

Running form is most efficient when you don't feel any noticeable effort, when running is almost automatic.

Over several years, your running form usually becomes more efficient—even when you feel "clunky." It's almost always better to go with the natural flow of your legs and body—even if you don't look like a star. In other words, if nothing seems to be wrong with your form, don't try to fix it. But if you're experiencing some of the form-related problems noted at the end of this chapter or others, I'll offer my prescription for moving easier.

ONCE A BODY IS IN MOTION...

Distance running is not a strength activity. Instead of overcoming gravity, we're trying to minimize its effect by staying low to the ground and reducing extraneous body motion. By going slowly in the beginning, it's easy to get moving, and, once in motion, the body wants to stay in motion. There are three components I use to monitor and fine-tune running form: posture, bounce and overstride.

POSTURE: RELAXED AND UPRIGHT

Don't try to be a Marine at attention. The best posture for running, walking or cruising is just good posture, with all elements

How to Run a Half or Full Marathon Efficiently

Running form is most efficient when you don't feel any noticeable effort, when running is almost automatic.

- Feet should stay low to the ground—no noticeable knee lift.

- Upright posture—Your body should be balanced with head over shoulders, over hips, so that no muscle power is needed to keep the body in position.

- Stay light on your feet. Those who want to improve times should increase turnover rate instead of stride length. (Turnover is the number of times your feet touch each minute.)

- The feet do not spring dramatically off the ground; they gently "lift off" in a reflex action as the body rolls forward.

- During most runs, concentrate on eliminating discomfort and noticeable effort in the exercising muscles. Strive to feel relaxed, comfortable and smooth.

relaxed and balanced as the foot comes underneath. A forward lean forces you to shorten your stride and creates extra tension on the lower back and neck. A backward lean is unusual but will also produce a shorter stride, loss of power from the running stride and possible tension in the lower back.

Some will argue that a forward lean will help you run faster, but I've found this to help only for a hundred yards or so. It forces you to work harder and therefore spends resources which are not available later in the run – causing you to lose more time than you gained during the short burst. The only exception I've found to this rule is when running on a gradual, downhill grade. A slight forward lean can help you run faster, and the boost from downhill gravity will offset the decrease in stride length. By having this slight monitor on downhill stride length, one can help counter the negative effect of overstriding, a temptation when running downhill.

CORRECTING FORWARD LEAN – by becoming a puppet on a string

Create a mental image during the form drill of yourself suspended from the very top of your head and shoulders by giant strings (as if you were a puppet). The effect is to lift you upright – head in line with shoulders and hips and everything lined up with each foot as it assumes the body's weight. A good puppet image also helps you to stay light on your feet.

The first effect of being a good puppet is to have your body line up without any tension – you're in balance. Walk around with the image of the puppet on the string until you feel relaxed in this upright position. Then start running slowly. Not only does the posture correct itself, but your chest is

forward as are your hips, allowing for a quick touch-off with the feet. You may have to make little adjustments, but when you're lined up in a relaxed mode, running will be easier.

BOUNCE

When in doubt, use less energy and stay lower to the ground, and you'll run smoother and quicker with better leg turnover. The energy spent in bouncing too high even by an inch is wasted—burned up in the air. The higher you lift yourself off the ground, the greater shock you have to absorb when landing and the longer it'll take for your feet and legs to recover from that run. Excess bounce also forces the legs to go through inefficient, extraneous motion during the extra time in the air. A higher back kick, for example, is the result of excess leg swing because your body is off the ground for an extra second or so. Such a kick produces early fatigue in the hamstring muscles.

You can correct bounce by keeping your feet close to the ground during sections of every run, especially when you feel the temptation to bounce (during the first mile and when going downhill). Instead of bouncing and spending energy, save your resources with a quick and light "lift-off" of the foot. You'll run about as fast by staying low to the ground with more steps per minute.

OVERSTRIDE

As the forward leg absorbs body weight, the lower leg should not be extended out in front of you.

146

CORRECTING OVERSTRIDE: Running easier

Our tendency to overstride is another attempt to counter slowing down with a quick fix. Unfortunately, our intuitive sense of pace gets us into trouble in this area. As runners get tired and realize that the main driving muscles are weakening due to fatigue, they subconsciously lengthen the stride to speed up. As in the case of other "quick fixes," this one will help only for a short distance.

Longer strides will over-stretch the muscles, causing them to tighten up later and weaken. If the stride is too long, it can put the knees or the muscles out of efficient mechanical range, increasing recovery time and causing injury. Everybody has "weak links," places that tend to get injured or sore most often. When the main driving muscles are tired, the knees wobble more and the "weak links" are likely to be pushed beyond their capacity. In other words, the damage will be greater.

When you feel tension in muscles which are at their limits – especially the calf and hamstring groups – you need to shorten the stride a bit more to relax them. Keep shortening the stride until the leg muscles relax. This may allow you to pick up the turnover of the feet and legs. But even if this increase doesn't happen, you'll reduce the chance of injury and speed up recovery due to the increased fatigue of overstriding. Often, the adjustment needed is a shortening of only an inch or two less than the overstride, but the relaxation it provides will allow the legs to go at a faster rhythm so that some runners can actually speed up at the end of the race.

As you pick up the turnover on form accelerations, be sure to keep the stride short enough so that the leg muscles are relaxed and can maintain a quick rhythm.

Cadence Drill (CD)

To correct overstride and keep feet low to the ground

The Research: Studies have clearly shown that as runners become faster, their stride length decreases. Therefore, the way to get faster is to increase turnover of feet and legs. Even those who lack a fast bone in their bodies will benefit from turnover drills because they teach the body to find a more efficient motion.

The Drill: After a slow mile warm-up, select a level and traffic-free stretch of road, trail or track. Without picking up your speed, count the number of times either your left foot or your right comes down in 30 seconds. Jog or walk for a minute or so and run back, counting again, with the goal of increasing the count by one or two. Repeat this four to six times, with the same projected increase each time but without a significant increase in effort.

How Often? If you do this drill once a week, you'll intuitively learn to stay low to the ground with an increasingly lighter touch of the foot. You'll see more progress when doing it twice. But you'll lose two weeks of progress if you miss a week.

147

TROUBLESHOOTING FORM PROBLEMS

QUADS *too tired, sore or weak*

When the main running muscles get tired, your stride length shortens as you slow down. The best strategy in this situation is to shorten the stride a little more and allow for a slight slowdown. Many runners, however, will try to maintain the same pace by using other muscles. The quadriceps on the front of your leg above the knee can allow this (for a while) by lifting the leg and maintaining a longer stride length. But the quads are not designed to do this and will fatigue easily. Afterward, you can usually count on two to four days of soreness, at least.

Sometimes quad soreness is directly related to running more downhill than you are used to running. Even when using a short stride while running downhill, some effort is required of the quadricep muscles—especially on long downhills. Many runners aggravate this by overstriding as they go down. Yes, it is tempting, and it is easy to extend the lower leg out in front of the body too much to pick up speed. To keep the legs and body under control, the quads must then be used as brakes. Not only is this an inefficient use of muscle power, but your quads will complain for several days afterward, especially after a long run. The recommended technique is to maintain a short stride and let gravity move you down with little effort.

Light exercise every day (such as walking on flat terrain) will speed up the recovery of sore quads. It is not a good idea to massage them, stretch them or exercise them too hard while they are sore.

BEHIND THE KNEE: *Discomfort, pain, or weakness*

Another sign of overstriding is pain or increased discomfort behind the knee. When you reach out further than you should with the lower leg, you're out of the knee's efficient range of motion. The full impact of your body's weight must be supported by the knee and through a mechanical range in which it is weakened. This is a hinge joint and was designed only to support body weight in the act of moving forward,

with the foot directly underneath. When your main running muscles become tired, they cannot give the knee any protection from this repeated abuse. As the tendons behind the knee become more stretched out during the run, the knee is forced to assume body weight in a straight or "locked out" position. Downhill running and faster running tend to bring on this problem.

Always try to maintain some bend in each knee when running. A shorter stride length will reduce the chance of this overstride problem. Do not try to stretch the tendons behind the knee at any time. Light massage with a chunk of ice can help. (Get a doctor's permission before using anti-inflammatory drugs.)

"WOBBLY" RUNNING FORM *at the end of long runs*

Most runners feel great at the beginning of long runs. It's natural to be tired at the end, but when the legs aren't supporting you well, you've overdone it in the beginning. The greatest downside of this condition is that you can easily aggravate your "weak links": those areas where you tend to experience injury.

This condition is totally preventable. Start the long ones a lot slower—at a pace that is at least two minutes slower per mile than you could run that distance on that day. It is also wise to take one-minute walk breaks every one to five minutes (from the beginning!).

SHOULDER AND NECK *muscles tired and tight*

If you're leaning forward as you run, you'll have a tendency to compensate by holding the head back, which uses the muscles of the shoulder and neck more and produces fatigue more rapidly. When the body is held upright, the head, neck and shoulders are in alignment and require little or no muscle power to keep them in position.

Those who hold their arms too far out from the body will also overextend the muscles of the shoulder and neck. The ideal arm motion is minimal, with the arms held in a relaxed position next to the body. When the lower arm goes through a small range of motion alongside the shorts and the upper part of the arm hardly moves, there is little fatigue in the arms, shoulders or neck muscles.

HAMSTRINGS *tired or sore*

You're lifting the foot behind you too far and/or extending stride too long. The longer stride is particularly a problem at the end of the long run as it overextends muscles like the hamstring, which are already tight and tired. Try to keep stride short, especially at the end of the run. Your back leg motion should have the lower part of the leg parallel to the horizon—at its highest elevation.

KNEE PAIN

When the main driving muscles get tired, they can no longer control your "safe" range of motion, and the resulting wobble can leave you in pain, sore or injured. A

slower early pace and walk breaks will help the legs stay fresh.

SORE FEET AND LOWER LEGS

You're pushing off the ground too hard and probably too high. Stay closer to the ground, lightly touching it, and maintain a short stride.

LOWER BACK *tired and sore*

You're leaning forward as you run. Straighten up and shorten stride.

STRETCHING WARNING: Even if your legs are tight after running, don't stretch at that time. A gentle period of massage and before bed will give you the benefits without as much risk of overstretching. Never try to "stretch out" a tight leg muscle during a run—except for the I-T Band.

Note: For more information on running form, see Galloway's Book on Running, *pp. 138-149.*

149

CROSS
TRAINING (XT)

THE XT DAYS

On non-running/walking days, cross training can give the attitude boost we need
while it bestows additional conditioning.
The best programs are those which are fun,
and therefore draw you back to do them
again and again. For this reason, many do
a variety of exercises in a single XT session to reduce the chance of boredom and
burnout.

XT CAN MAINTAIN CONDITIONING WHILE INJURED

Don't think that "it's over" if you come
down with an injury during a training
program. Over the years, I've met dozens
of runners and walkers who, while injured,
maintained conditioning through significant
crosstraining and were able to finish the
race comfortably. During an eight-week injury, one training group member ran in the
water and came back to do the marathon in
a personal best: under three hours!

THE BEST EXERCISES FOR MAINTAINING CONDITIONING

As in any form of conditioning, the best
exercises to get "back-ups" in shape for the
running/walking muscles are those which
best use the leg muscles in the same way.

Water running has produced the best effect
for large numbers of exercisers training for
a long distance event. Cross-country ski
machines have also produced a high level
of conditioning.

THE BEST EXERCISES FOR FAT-BURNING

Exercises which elevate the body temperature, keep it up, and use lots of muscle cells
are best. Cross-country ski machines, rowing machines, and then cycling and other
indoor machines can help to increase the
fat-burning effect.

BEWARE OF THE STAIR!

Stair machines use many of the muscles
used in running and walking. This means
that they aren't the best choice for alternative exercise on a rest day. But they can
simulate hills, to some extent, if you use
them occasionally to replace a running/
walking day (or as a second session on a
run/walk day).

GRADUALLY INTRODUCE THE MUSCLES TO XT

- Ease into each new exercise.

- For the first few weeks, don't do the
  same exercise every day.

Mon	Tue	Wed	Thu	Fri	Sat	Sun
H2O run	cycle	H2O run	swim	H2O run	off	long H2O run
strength	swim	strength	X-C ski machine	strength	swim	

- You can, however, do several different exercises which can be alternated.

- To get the best effect for the half or full marathon, it's better to use a slow continuous motion instead of quick, short bursts of high intensity.

EASING INTO NEW EXERCISES

- On the first day go five easy minutes, rest for 20 to 30 minutes, and then do another five minutes.

- You could start with two to three different exercises, alternating them and gradually increasing the session to one hour.

- During each successive session, increase by three to five minutes on each of the two segments.

- For example:

Session #

1 5min/5min
2 8min/8min
3 12min/12min
4 15min/15min
5 18min/18min
6 22min/22min

- Exercise every day at first, if you wish, building up to two 30-minute sessions.

  - You may then combine the exercise into one continuous session with a frequency of every other day. On the off day, you may do a different exercise routine.

IF INJURED:

- Don't do any exercise which could aggravate the injured area.

- Try to simulate the same intensity and duration of your scheduled workout session for that day. For example, if a long one were scheduled, estimate the length of the time you'd be exercising and spend that time continuously running or walking in the water, on the cross-country ski machine, etc. As you're doing the alternative exercise, try to maintain about the same level of exertion as you would feel in a regular training session.

GRADUALLY WORK INTO NEW EXERCISES

- Build up to about the same duration and intensity of exercise you'd be doing if running or walking.

- You can alternate back and forth between many exercises to keep the activity interesting.

151

- Never push the muscles to the point of tiredness or loss of strength in individual exercises or in the session as a whole.

IF YOU'RE NOT INJURED BUT ARE JUST ADDING EXTRA FITNESS TO YOUR PROGRAM...

- Choose a variety of exercises for your non-running/walking days.

- You don't need to do any one of the exercises for more than about 10 minutes, if you don't want to. By alternating between activities, you'll tend to avoid boredom.

- Water running and cross-country ski machines are the best for runners and walkers.

152

BENEFITS OF WATER RUNNING AND WALKING

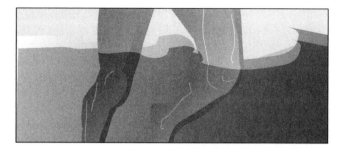

BENEFITS OF WATER RUNNING/ WALKING

• Legs must find the most efficient mechanical path through the water. Extraneous motions of the feet and legs are reduced or eliminated over time.

• The water's resistance strengthens muscles which can serve as back-up strength to the primary running/walking muscles. By alternating off and on, the main running/walking muscles will retain resiliency longer. These smaller "reserve" muscles will also be able to keep you going for a little while if you overuse the main running/walking muscles and need some help to keep going during the last few miles in the half or full marathon.

• You get a great cardiovascular training session without any pounding. Since the prime running/walking muscles are not being used, most injuries can heal.

WATER TRAINING TECHNIQUES

THE RUNNING/WALKING MOTION

This is the same form one would use when running or walking efficiently on land. The body should be upright, not stiff. A slight

forward lean is okay, but don't lean too far. The ideal motion is a smooth one, getting quick turnover. Focus on finding the most efficient path through the water. In this way you'll be cutting out mechanical inefficiencies and encouraging an efficient stride on land.

• Knees don't come up very far.

• Lower legs and feet are kicked forward.

• The whole leg is brought behind you, with knee slightly bent.

• Back leg bends to a right angle and then returns forward.

• Arms can be moved through a range of motion similar to that of regular running. Don't exaggerate the arm swing.

CROSS-COUNTRY (X-C) SKI MOTION

This strengthening exercise should be done in short segments of 10 seconds to a minute. By weaving segments into the marathon motion, you'll increase strength in the quadriceps (front of thigh), hamstrings, butt muscles, hip flexors and lower back.

• The legs are almost completely straight.

Note: Water running is easier when you use a flotation device, in the deeper water, so that your legs can move through one of the motions listed above.

- The range of motion is about 20 percent longer than the marathon motion.

- Move the legs like a scissors through the water.

Start each segment with a short range of motion, gradually extending it. Over time, you may increase both range of motion and speed, but be careful. Remember that you're building strength and not anaerobic performance. Never extend any motion to the point that you feel at your mechanical limits. And don't work too long in the X-C ski motion so that you're out of breath.

THE SPRINT

For those who have been doing speed play and don't want to risk injury while in a long distance program, the sprint motion can keep the speed components in good form without the risk of pounding or interval training injuries.

154

- Shorten your marathon motion to about half.

- Keep legs and feet directly underneath you.

- Pick up the turnover of your legs and feet so that you're going through the leg pat-

tern about twice as fast as the marathon motion.

This shouldn't be a true sprint (going all out) because you want to go at a pace that you could continue for one to two minutes. You will be huffing and puffing through the second half of each of these, as they are anaerobic. Start each "sprint segment" by gradually increasing the turnover. The short range of motion directly underneath you will cause your head and shoulders to rise out of the water somewhat. The arm motion should also be a shortened version of the marathon motion to keep up with the legs.

CAUTIONS:

- Make sure that the water running/walking motion is within efficient mechanical range.

- If you're injured, get clearance from your doctor that you're not aggravating the injury.

- Don't overtrain. Just going through an efficient water running/walking motion will bestow benefits. You don't have to push it.

BREATHING

*B*y using an efficient breathing technique, you'll not only be capable of a higher level of performance, but you'll also teach yourself how to acquire a better supply of oxygen and improve almost every aspect of your exercise experience.

THE CONCEPT OF DEEP BREATHING (ALSO CALLED "BELLY BREATHING")

◆ You're filling up the lower part of the lungs first.

◆ Through practice you can quickly inhale and quickly exhale while deep breathing.

◆ You don't need to fill the upper part of your lungs to capacity.

ELIMINATING SIDE PAINS

The deep-breathing technique can help you reduce or eliminate those irritating side pains which often erupt just when you're getting into your exercise. Such pains seem to be primarily caused by shallow breathing—using the upper part of our lungs in a minimal way. This low energy expenditure method is adequate for our normal sedentary activities and seems to provide

sufficient oxygen at the beginning of an exercise session. But it also minimizes the amount of oxygen which you could absorb during exertion and often puts you into debt. If you start your runs and walks with shallow breathing, you'll probably get side pains during some of them. Since side pains are aggravated by going out faster than you should (even when the pace feels easy), slow down at the beginning of all of your workouts if you've been experiencing these discomforts.

155

DEEP-BREATHING TECHNIQUE

◆ Quickly exhale as completely as possible every third or fourth breath.

◆ This almost guarantees a complete intake as you inhale immediately afterward.

◆ Breathe normally in between the deeper breaths.

◆ Don't do this deeper breathing more often because you could hyperventilate.

◆ You must start this technique from the beginning of your workout session to maximize its effect.

Some folks time their exhale to take place as they push off, every second or third step. If this sounds intriguing, try it two ways: 1) breathe out completely as you push off either the right or the left foot or 2) alternate between the left or right foot. To see which method works best, you should attempt one method only during a specific run/walk.

You can practice this breathing method at any time—not just when exercising. Be sure to start each exercise session using this technique. After several weeks or months of regular breathing in this way, it will become your almost automatic breathing method.

Note: For more information on breathing, see Galloway's Book On Running, *pp. 143-144.*

STRETCHING

THE GOOD NEWS:

If you have found stretches that work for you, do them if you wish. But be careful: many runners/walkers are injured by stretching. I believe that most are better off not stretching. I absolve you of any guilt you might have from not stretching.

THE BAD NEWS:

Stretching is the third leading cause of injury among runners/walkers. While these injuries are almost always the result of improper technique, it is very easy to injure yourself while doing a stretch that seems perfectly safe.

STRETCHING DOES NOT WARM YOU UP FOR A RUN/WALK

The best warm-up for running or walking has been the following: 1) easy walking, 2) walking, 3) very slow jogging and then change, 4) gradually picking up your pace to "normal." Stretching before a workout will not warm you up better or sooner, and it won't help you go faster in that workout.

DON'T!

- Don't stretch when you're in a hurry.

- Don't stretch before running/walking.

- Don't try to "stretch out" a tired or tight muscle.

- Don't stretch a tight muscle during or immediately after a run/walk.

- Don't stretch immediately after running/walking (wait at least 30 minutes).

Note: Those who suffer from iliotibial band injury can usually benefit from stretching this band.

STRENGTH TRAINING

**Strong and balanced postural muscles will
keep you upright when you're fatigued, improving
your breathing and oxygen intake, as
you maintain strength and efficiency.**

I don't believe that we need to do any
strength exercises to run or walk. If you
have any doubts, look at the "toothpick"
legs of the winners of any major marathon.
It's obvious that they don't spend time in
the gym. Running or walking is easier and
more fun when we spend a little energy to
get moving and then fine-tune our movements to take advantage of our momentum.
*Read more about this in the Running Form
and Walking Form chapters in this book
and in* Galloway's Book on Running.

I do, however, recommend a couple of
strength exercises for long-term postural
support. I discovered this after my arms and
shoulders became increasingly more tired on
long runs in the mid-1980's. By doing the
exercises listed below, I've virtually eliminated that type of fatigue even when going
long distances.

Legs can be strengthened most efficiently by
doing regular hill training (see the chapter
in this book). Running and walking up an
incline forces the leg muscles to perform
against natural resistance in the act of running or walking. By doing artificial weight
exercises, you can upset the natural balance
that has developed between the muscle
groups. Such an imbalance can cause injury.

POSTURAL STRENGTH EXERCISES

I've found that a bare minimum of strength
training can keep the postural muscles
strong and balanced. These muscles maintain the upper body in a relaxed but upright
position. When neglected, they slowly
weaken. Over a 10-year period, individuals gradually slump and stoop a little more.
Runners and walkers notice this sooner. On
long or hard runs, those with weak postural
muscles will lose their form more quickly
and experience more aches and pains. A
slumping upper body also reduces breathing efficiency. After starting with about 10
exercises in the late 1980's, I gradually
evolved down to the two which are noted
below. The "crunch" strengthens the front
of the body, and "arm running" strengthens
the muscles of the lower back, upper back,
shoulders and neck. But if you're looking for beach muscles, this isn't the right
program.

THE CRUNCH

This is the old sit-up, with the range of motion reduced significantly. By keeping the
body near the floor and constantly using
the muscles, you get a lot of good strengthening in a short amount of time.

This exercises the upper abdominal group (the "six-pack").

HERE'S HOW:

- Lie down on your back on a padded surface with your knees bent.

- Raise your upper torso very slightly off the floor (lower back still touching the surface). Lift and lower only three to five inches or so until the muscles fatigue.

- Don't continue until the muscles give out or burn.

ARM RUNNING

This exercise is done in the standing position with legs spread about as wide as your shoulders (or less wide if this is not comfortable). You can experiment a little bit with the motion, but don't do anything which will put your back at risk. It's always safer when you use handheld weights to keep them close to the body.

HERE'S HOW:

- Stand upright and relaxed with your feet spread about the width of your shoulders.

- Use handheld weights in both hands. Choose a weight that will give you a little challenge but is not a struggle.

- Move the arms through the motion you'd use when running, keeping the hands close to the body.

- Starting with two to three repetitions, increase by one rep each session until you get up to 10.

- To see results, you need to do this two to three times a week

- I do several sets of 10, spread throughout the day, three days a week.

Note: If you want to develop strength, it helps to see a strength expert. The advice above is only given as one runner to another. Never do any exercise that could pull or strain a muscle, back, etc.

COLD WEATHER
RUNNING/WALKING

*E*xperts in extreme temperature research tell me that even when the temperature drops below -30° F (without the wind) there's no reason to be concerned about lung damage. There are so many buffer zones in your respiratory system that prevent outside air from impacting any area deeper than your throat—and masks can prevent problems there. By putting on the right combination of layers, fabrics, extremity protectors and skin care products, you can enjoy being out on very cold days, like the runners and walkers of Alaska, Minnesota and the ice belt of Canada.

DRESSING: DON'T BE HELD HOSTAGE BY THE WEATHER. VISIT A GOOD RUNNING, WALKING OR SKI STORE AND FIND OUT WHAT TO WEAR.

1. Wear a series of thin layers. Close to your skin, you'll want something warm. Polypro is one of a series of winter fibers that keep the warmth close to the skin but allow extra heat and perspiration to escape.

2. Continue to add external layers, adjusting to the temperature and wind conditions.

3. Cover up all extremities with extra layering: hands, ears, toes.

4. Men, wear an extra layer or two as underwear, as you need.

5. In extreme cold (when temperature or wind chill is below 10° F/11° C), do not expose any skin, if possible. Even when there is minimal exposure, put Vaseline or other cold weather insulation/protection on any area which may incidentally be hit by the wind (eyelids, etc).

6. Be sure to coat your shoes or use socks that insulate your feet. Most running shoes are designed to let heat out and cold into your feet, which can cause frostbite on days colder than 32° F or 0° C. Remember that you generate a significant wind chill effect on your feet as you move them through the running or walking motion.

7. As you warm up through exercise, peel off each layer before you start sweating. Too much sweat accumulation will freeze and cause problems.

WARM-UPS THAT TAKE THE STING OUT OF WINTER

1. On very cold days, bundle up and exercise for a very few minutes indoors. You may walk, jog in place, use an indoor track, or exercise on the machines (cycle, rowing, stair, etc.) Before you start

sweating, go outdoors and you'll have a reservoir of warmth to get you down the road.

2. Start your run or walk going into the wind. This allows you to come back with the wind.

3. If you start to get very warm, remove an outside layer of clothing or unzip your outer layer, if applicable. A garment with long sleeves allows you to tie it around your waist or put it in your fanny pack—because you may need it later.

4. On cold days, pick environments where

you could seek refuge for at least a few minutes if you need to.

5. On very cold or windy days, alternate between inside and out. If you have an indoor facility, it helps to come inside when you start to get cold. Exercise indoors only long enough to take the sting away—but head outdoors before you start sweating.

6. Don't let yourself sweat because it is likely to freeze and leave you very cold. Remove a layer or go outside before the sweat starts flowing.

Clothing Thermometer

What to wear as it gets colder (In Fahrenheit)

60° +	Tank top or singlet and shorts
50°-59°	T-shirt and shorts
40°-49°	Long sleeve T, shorts or tights or wind pants, socks or mittens or gloves
30°-39°	Long sleeve T and T-shirt, tights and shorts, socks or mittens or gloves and hat over ears
20°-29°	Polypro top or thick long sleeve T, another T-shirt layer, tights and shorts, mittens or gloves, and hat over ears
10°-19°	Polypro top and thick long sleeve T, tights and shorts, wind suit (top and pants), thick mittens, thick hat over ears
0°-9°	Two polypro tops, thick tights and shorts (and thick underwear or supporter for men), Goretex or similar thickness warm-up, gloves and thick mittens, ski mask and hat over ears, and Vaseline covering any exposed skin
-15° to -1°	Two thick polypro tops, tights and thick polypro tights and thick underwear (and supporter for men), thick warm-up, gloves, thick (arctic) ski mask and thick hat over ears, Vaseline covering any exposed skin, thicker socks on feet and other measures for feet, as needed
-20° and below	Add layers as needed. Stay in touch with the outdoor and ski shops for the warmest clothing which is thin. Watch your feet. There are some socks which heat up...and other innovations.

Note: Cotton is not recommended next to your skin. I suggest using one of the technical fibers.

Note: These are only recommendations; use the combination of layers which works best for you.

HOT WEATHER
RUNNING AND WALKING

*T*here's good and bad news about exercising in the heat. First, the bad news: when the temperature rises above 55° F (10° C), you're going to go slower and feel worse than you will at lower temperatures. But by gradually preparing yourself for increased temperatures and taking action from the beginning of hot weather workouts, you'll get a welcome dose of the good news. You'll learn how to hydrate yourself, what to wear, and when and how much your body can take in hot weather. All of this will help you recover faster and exercise better than others of your ability on hot days. While even the most heat-trained runners or walkers won't go as fast on hot days as on cold ones, they won't slow down as much nor will they feel as much discomfort once they've trained in the heat.

Note: Be sure to read the next section, Heat Disease Alert. Many exercisers get into serious trouble even on moderately warm days without knowing it. Mark this section and revisit it several times during the warm season of the year. Anyone who has heart disease risk factors or suspicions of these should talk to a doctor trained in exercise before continuing.

Until the temperature rises to about 65° F, most runners and walkers don't notice much heat buildup, even though it is al-

ready putting extra burdens on the system. It takes most folks about 30 to 45 minutes of exercising (with or without walk breaks) to feel warm. But soon after that, if the temperature is above about 60° F/14° C, you're suddenly hot and sweating. In training sessions and especially races under those conditions, most exercisers have to force themselves to slow down. It's just too easy to start faster than you should when it's 60° to 69° F because it feels cool at first.

As the mercury rises above 60° F, your body can't get rid of the heat buildup. This causes a rise in core body temperature, leading to an early depletion of fluids through sweating. The internal temperature rise also triggers rapid dispersion of blood into the capillaries of the skin, reducing the amount of that vital fluid that is available to the exercising muscles. Just when these workhorses are being pushed to top capacity, they are receiving less oxygen and nutrients due to reduced blood flow. What used to be a river becomes a creek and can't remove the waste products of exercise (such as lactic acid). As these accumulate, your muscles slow down.

Even the most heat-conditioned athletes will record slower times in warm weather. The harder you exercise in hot weather, especially from the beginning, the longer

How to stay cool (55° F/10° C or above)

- **Slow down early:** The later you wait to do this, the more dramatically you'll slow down at the end and the longer it will take to recover. Walk/shuffle breaks, early and often, help you lower the exertion level, which conserves resources for the end and reduces heat buildup.

- **Wear lighter garments and not cotton:** Loose-fitting clothes allow heat to escape. Don't wear cotton clothing. Sweat soaks into cotton, causing it to cling to your skin, increasing heat buildup. Several materials will wick the perspiration away from your skin: Coolmax, polypro, etc. As the moisture leaves your skin area, you receive a cooling effect, and these types of materials allow this to happen.

- **Pour our water over yourself.** You lose up to 70 percent of the heat you can lose through the top of your head so regularly pour water there (even if you're like me, "hair challenged"). Regularly pouring water on a light, polypro (or a similar material) singlet or tank top will keep you cooler.

- **Don't wear a hat!** Hats keep your heat from being released through the best vent you have, the top of your head. Don't cover it up.

- **Drink cold water.** Not only does cold water leave the stomach quicker than any type of fluid, it produces a slight physiological cooling effect—and an even greater psychological cooling effect. But don't drink too much either. Most of us do well with 14-20 ounces an hour during warm weather. Good research says that we shouldn't drink more than 27 oz. (800 ml) per hour.

- **Take a dip or a shower.** On hot days, you can significantly reduce heat buildup if you spend three to four minutes in a pool or cold shower every mile or two. Do this several times and even the hottest day's run becomes manageable. The break in your workout will not cause you to get out of shape. Over the span of a month, most walkers/runners get in more training this way because they don't overheat early.

- **Don't eat a big meal.** Eating too much, particularly meals that are high in protein or fat, will put extra stress on your system when you exercise. Even worse is the probability that too much food loading will lead to unloading. Instead of big meals, eat light snacks, which you know will digest easily, every hour or two. Many exercisers find that they must not eat anything within two hours or so of their hot weather workout (although an energy bar or energy gel works well for most).

163

it takes to recover. But it's also possible to take action from the start to reduce muscle damage, speed recovery, and even finish better in races.

Humidity. The higher the humidity, the quicker you'll feel the effect of the heat and the more difficult it will be to continue. Watch the weather reports and install a temperature and humidity gauge at your house. After a while, you'll learn the combination of the two which causes you discomfort so that you can avoid the times of the day when those conditions arise.

Body Fat. The more body fat you have, the worse you'll feel as the temperature rises. I don't have any research on this, but my experience tells me that for every increase of five percent in body fat, the effects of heat and humidity are felt three to five minutes sooner. For example, if a runner or walker with 12 percent body fat feels severe heat discomfort at 45 minutes, then a 22 percent runner/walker feels it around 35 minutes, and a 32 percent runner/walker feels it around 25 minutes. Body fat acts like a blanket to hold heat in. It does too good a job during the summer.

The best time for hot weather exercise is before the sun comes up. The earlier the better, relative to how you'll feel later in the day. The second best time to get out, by the way, is right after sunrise, unless the temperature cools off dramatically at sunset, then that time period would present a great opportunity. In humid areas, however, it usually doesn't cool down much after sunset.

Training for hot weather

One day a week, you can train yourself to deal with the heat by inserting the hot segments below into your workout, even if you are starting in the middle of winter. Of course, you need to get in at least two other days per week, and you must do this heat training day every week. Before doing each hot segment, read the page that follows this chapter on heat disease. At the first indication of symptoms, stop the workout before you get into trouble. The process of heat training follows the same principles of conditioning for endurance and speed. By pushing yourself a little bit and then backing off, your body makes adaptations to better deal with heat the next time.

Week #	# of minutes of hot segment
1	5-7 minutes
2	7-9 minutes
3	9-12 minutes
4	12-16 minutes
5	16-22 minutes
6	22-26 minutes

On each of these sessions, warm up for at least 10 minutes of easy running/walking and ease off with at least 10 minutes of easy running and walking after the heat phase. If the outdoor temperature is cool, you may put on one or more layers of clothes, especially on the upper body, during the hot segment. You may also do these segments indoors. Run or walk at a very easy pace on these segments. You're only working on heat adaptation.

Adjusting for heat

As the weather gets hotter, you must slow down your pace from the beginning: 30 seconds per mile slower for every five degree increase in temperature above 60°F.

Heat Disease Alert

*T*he most common health problem among endurance exercisers is heat disease. This is a serious condition which has resulted in death in a high percentage of cases, even in highly trained, young athletes.

PREVENTION:

- During hot weather, exercise at the coolest time (usually before sunrise).

- Drink water all day long.

- Avoid caffeine, alcohol and other drugs.

- Wear clothing that is light and loose.

- Eat small, lowfat snacks which you know will not cause you distress (far enough ahead).

- Don't significantly increase duration or intensity.

- Slow down pace even more to adjust for heat, humidity and hills—especially in the beginning.

- Take walk breaks more often on hot days.

SYMPTOMS:

- Intense heat buildup in the head, significant headache, general overheating of the body

- General confusion and loss of concentration and muscular control

- Over-sweating and then cessation of sweating, clammy skin and excessive breathing

- Extreme tiredness, upset stomach, muscle cramps, vomiting, feeling faint

RISK FACTORS:

- Sleep deprivation

- Infection (viral, bacterial, etc.)

- Dehydration (avoid alcohol and caffeine)

- Severe sunburn, skin irritation

- Unaccustomed to hot weather

- Overweight

- Untrained for specific training session

- Occurrence(s) of heat disease in the past

- Under medications—especially the following: cold medicines, diuretics, medicines for diarrhea, tranquilizers, antihistamines, atropine and scopolamine

- The following medical conditions: high cholesterol, high blood pressure, under extreme stress, asthma, diabetes, epilepsy, drug use (including alcohol), cardiovascular disease, smoking, unfit lifestyle

SEE A PHYSICIAN WHO KNOWS THE BENEFICIAL EFFECTS OF RUNNING AND FITNESS

- Before beginning the program

- If you have any question about any of the above conditions

- If you notice any significant change in body functions, immune response, etc.

TAKE ACTION!

- Watch for heat disease in group members and take action if you think they are in trouble.

- Walk, cool off and get help immediately

166

HEART RATE MONITORS IN A TRAINING PROGRAM

Note: Before using a heart rate monitor, you must be tested for maximum heart rate. The tables or formulas based on age are only averages and should not be used to determine whether you're overtraining or not. Testing should be done under the supervision of a trained professional. You don't need to go through a Maximum Oxygen Uptake test; the Max Heart Rate test is sufficient and not as involved.

• If your estimate of max heart rate is too low, you'll not receive maximum benefit from using the heart monitor on speed sessions. You're wasting one of the primary sources of biofeedback which the heart monitor can give.

• If your max heart rate estimate is too high, you'll overtrain on speed sessions and risk a long recovery time. It's also possible to overtrain on easy days and not recover between the harder sessions.

When Heart Monitors can help

1. To hold you back during a long one—especially at the end

2. To make sure that an easy day is really easy

3. To ensure that "form accelerations" are "easy gliders"

4. To help you improve racing form—without overtraining

5. To keep you from having a long recovery after speed sessions

6. To tell you when you have rested enough between repetitions in a speed session

7. To serve notice when you're overtrained and need to take some extra days off or easy

8. To make sure that you're going slowly enough on the easy days

When Heart Monitors don't help

1. At the beginning of long ones (especially if you try to stay close to 70 percent max heart rate)

2. When you don't know your exact maximum heart rate

HOLDING YOU BACK ON A LONG ONE

Almost everyone is capable of going faster for three to six miles than they can run for 15 or more. If you wear your heart monitor on a long training workout and try to stay at 70 percent of maximum heart rate, you'll almost certainly go too hard at first, which will make the end of the session difficult and increase recovery time.

The reason for this is as follows: at the start of a long one, you can run or walk slower than you could race a 5K or 10K and feel very comfortable for the first few miles. Running or fast walking that pushes you to 70 percent of max heart rate means that you're at 70 percent of your 5K or 10K pace, which is almost certainly too fast for a long one that exceeds 15 miles.

In other words, you can go too fast during the first part of a long training session and still register a heart rate of less than 70 percent of maximum heart rate.

Use the two-minute rule instead of your heart monitor during the first part of the long ones: Go at least two minutes per mile slower than the "magic mile" predicts in a half or full marathon. This means that you must adjust for heat, humidity, hills, etc. If your pace is slower than this, you'll only benefit from a faster recovery, while receiving the same endurance value as a fast workout of the same distance.

The heart monitor can help you regulate subconscious increases in effort between pace checks. I recommend staying below 65 percent of max heart rate for the first half of the long one, during which period you'll probably notice an elevated rate on the hills (telling you to slow down). During the second half, the gradual onset of fatigue will cause the heart rate to naturally rise at the same effort level. Adjust pace to keep the rate below 70 percent during the second half.

MAKING SURE THAT AN EASY DAY IS REALLY AN EASY DAY

The easy workouts during the week merely maintain the conditioning you gained on the weekend long one. To ensure that you're going slowly enough, wear your heart monitor and stay below 65 percent of max. This conservative plan will limit the possibility of going too hard when you need to be recovering.

RACE REHEARSAL SEGMENTS: SHOULD I RUN A HALF OR FULL MARATHON PACE MILES DURING THE WEEK?

If you've recovered from the weekend long or hard training sessions, it's beneficial for time goal runners or walkers to run at event pace on the Tuesday and Thursday easy runs. Here are some heart monitor guidelines for going at goal pace during some segments of easy day workouts:

1. Do a slow warm-up, ensuring that heart rate is significantly below 70 percent of max heart rate. If there are any signs of tiredness, just go slowly for the rest of the session.

2. After one to two slow miles, do four to eight acceleration-GLIDERS. These will help your form to become smoother while you become comfortable running at a faster rhythm.

3. As you start the first mile at event pace, monitor your heart rate. Ideally, the rate will stay around 70 percent of maximum, but it's okay if it creeps a bit higher. If the rate reaches 75 percent of max, and you're not going faster than goal pace, just go slowly for the rest of

the session. This is a sign that you're still fatigued from earlier sessions.

Note: for more information, see my book, A Year Round Plan.

KEEPING YOUR "FORM ACCELERATIONS" FROM BECOMING SPRINTS

The purpose of gliding fast during some of your easy weekday workouts is to work on more efficient form. You want these quicker turnover "glides" of 20-30 steps or so to be at a faster pace than you would go normally but without a significant increase in effort or heart rate. The heart monitor can give you this check on reality. If the rate rises above 75 percent on an acceleration, shorten stride, keep feet lower to the ground, avoid pushing off hard and glide fast. This should keep the heart rate from getting out of bounds.

TO HELP YOU IMPROVE RACING FORM

Your speed sessions can develop the endurance-speed needed for the race. With the help of the heart monitor, you have the biofeedback necessary to improve form at the same time.

Each repeat should only be about 30 seconds faster per mile than your goal pace. By using a heart monitor, you can teach yourself to run or walk more efficiently, finding form innovations which help you run or walk more smoothly. Let's say that during the first two repeats, your heart rate goes up to between 75 and 80 percent of max heart rate. On the remaining repeats, maintain the same pace and try to keep the heart rate from going beyond 75 percent by moving more efficiently. *See the chapters on Running Form and Walking Form for suggestions for improvement.*

MONITORS WILL TELL YOU WHEN YOU CAN START ANOTHER REPEAT——AND TO HELP SPEED RECOVERY.

By keeping your monitor on during the rest interval, you can tell when you have recovered enough to do another one. You should wait until the heart rate has gone below 70 percent and then walk for at least another 100 meters or so. It is better to let the heart rate drop to below 65 percent of max, if possible. This extra rest will improve recovery.

MONITORS TELL YOU WHETHER YOU'VE OVERTRAINED

Some exercisers wear their monitor at night during hard training. Note the lowest rate during the night. After a few weeks, you'll establish a base line which tells you what your heart rate averages.

- When your resting heart rate (taken under the same conditions, day after day) is five percent higher than the low baseline, take an easy day.

- When the rate climbs to 10 percent or more higher than your low baseline, take the day off. You may do some non-pounding exercise if desired.

169

THE POWER OF THE GROUP

- As a team, you can share the challenges, the laughs, the struggles and the exhilaration.

- No one needs to go through a tough day without being bolstered by the others.

- As you give support, you'll receive much more in return.

- Every year, in just about every pace group, lifelong friendships are formed.

I'm very proud of the over 98 percent completion rate among those who go through the Galloway Training Program. I can't take credit for this rate of success, however. It's the fun and the bonding that occurs in each pace group as individuals become a team. In a group, those who have trouble getting motivated get on track. Competitors who tend to get injured from pushing too hard by themselves stay back with the group and stay healthy.

Much of the credit for the upsurge in half and full marathon completion goes to the groups that are springing up across North America. Individuals training alone usually reach a plateau of fatigue, injury, lack of motivation or complications in other areas of life and drop out of the program. As the members of the group share the anxiety of the challenge of the event, they respond in interesting ways by becoming a closer group and inspiring one another.

If there's not a group in your area, you can start one by training together with just one other person. Many lonely exercisers will call friends and talk until they're motivated to get out the door. Some have simulated group workouts by talking on cell phones during long ones.

It's interesting to watch the groups come together. On the first day together, most are feeling a bit shy, reluctant to say much more than polite conversation. But after another group run or two, each member develops a sense of belonging and trust for the others. Over the next few months, often without realizing it, each will need to pull at least a little support from teammates, and each will give the same to the others. Through the joking and the gut-level respect generated through meeting challenges together, bonds are established which last a lifetime. Starting as ordinary fitness people, you'll rise to the extraordinary challenge of the half or full marathon.

BACK TO OUR ROOTS

The primitive satisfaction we feel in group runs brings us directly back to our roots. Our ancestors migrated in small gatherings and developed a lot of human social skills along the way. In many cases, survival depended upon the successful completion of the migration and the ability to work together physically, mentally and spiritually. In a different way, our cardiovascular survival depends upon our weekly migrations.

Certainly, the varied and significant rewards of the migration are programmed into our being by these hearty ancestors. When we reach the finish line of each long one, we experience an unusual sense of genuine accomplishment, which is the same type experienced by Phidippides and a continuous stream of ancestors before him, going back at least a million years.

Some companies are discovering that the power of half or full marathon team-building improves the bottom line as it reduces the waistline. I've seen how this experience breaks down barriers between divisions within a corporation as even the non-exercisers pull for the trainees to meet the challenge. You can't buy the productivity and attitude benefits that come from such a program.

BONDING WITH OTHERS...AND SELF

The most successful groups are those composed of folks at the same conditioning level. Together, this team of fitness equals will share the challenges, the exhilaration and the human moments. Because of the group, no one will go through a tough day without begin bolstered by the others. All will share the uplifting successes of each, in training and the other areas of life. As you give support, you'll receive much more in return.

GROUP FUN

The primary goal of each group is to have fun as the distance is covered. I'm not saying that every step is wonderful or every hill bestows joy, but as you exchange jokes and stories and let the chemistry of your personalities create a unique group identity, the fun will emerge. At first you may have to search for it and use your imagination. Soon you'll enjoy a continuous stream of very short but spontaneous moments of humor which bring the marathon experience to life.

HOMEWORK ASSIGNMENT: A JOKE, A JUICY STORY AND A CONTROVERSIAL ISSUE

If everyone brings each of these to every workout, group entertainment is guaranteed. Sometimes it takes only one issue, and you can't believe that you're nearing the end. Many groups give awards at breakfast afterward: the juiciest story wins a big orange juice.

KEEP THE GROUP TOGETHER— USING THE "HUFF & PUFF" RULE

In each of the Galloway training locations, we subdivide into pace groups based upon current conditioning and background. But even in the most "equal" groupings, one or two individuals may struggle from time to time. It doesn't hurt a faster runner or walker to slow down, for the endurance is based on the distance covered, not the pace. So the group adjusts the pace to accommodate the members who just aren't having a good day (more frequent walk or shuffle breaks, slower pace, etc.).

If someone is huffing and puffing during the first half, slow the pace down at that time, even if the slower person tells the others to leave him or her behind. During the last two to three miles, huffing is going to occur, but it shouldn't keep the individual from carrying on a conversation. If this occurs, not only does the group need to slow down for the last few miles, but on the next long one, the pace should be adjusted slower from the beginning.

ADJUSTING

During the first few weeks the groups will be a bit fluid, and some of you will want to move up or down. Please take the advice of your group leader if he or she suggests that another group's pace would be more comfortable for you. The first group priority is that everyone feel comfortable so that the "team" can stay together. Those who are faster must slow down to keep from producing injury or severe fatigue in the slower members. It doesn't hurt anyone to slow down. Faster runners and walkers who "throttle back" receive the same endurance and will recover faster. If you're not sure that you're in the correct group, consult your group leader. The best time to change groups, should this be necessary, is during the first three to four weeks, but it's okay to change after that.

GROUP RULES

1. Help the group leader by supporting the walk/shuffle breaks and keeping the pace slow. Also, help with water, refreshments, etc.

2. Everyone in the group should be able to carry on a conversation, even at the end. If anyone is huffing and puffing at all in the first half, slow the pace down and/or take more frequent breaks.

3. Take all of the walk/shuffle breaks, early and often. As the long ones get longer, the breaks should be taken more frequently.

4. If you're feeling tired (or you sense that someone else is struggling), tell the group leader so that the pace can be slowed.

5. When you're feeling great, slow down and stay with the group—don't lead them astray!

6. Each member of the group is responsible for his or her own safety. Never assume that others are looking out for you.

7. Your health is your responsibility. Get checked out by a doctor who knows about endurance exercise; confer with him or her when needed. Get help before medical problems occur.

8. Wear the shirt of your group in case you get separated.

9. Drink about every two miles but no more than 27 oz (800 ml) per hour.

10. Keep it fun. Bring a joke, a juicy story and a controversial issue and share.

DON'T CUT OUT ANY WALK/ SHUFFLE BREAKS

In every group, there are a few macho folks who push for eliminating the first few breaks. Hey, these are the most important ones! By starting early and doing each one, you'll speed up the recovery for every person in the group.

YOU'RE IN THE PROCESS OF BECOMING A MEMBER OF AN ELITE GROUP

About two tenths of one percent of the population completes a half or full marathon each year. At the same time that most of the population is decreasing exercise and getting obese, your group is getting fitter. The dropout rate among individuals training on their own is about 20 times as high as those who join groups with pace groups. While most individual runners become injured or drop out of their training during the last six weeks, Galloway pace group programs have almost no dropout during this same period.

Group energy and support creates a bonding and level of respect experienced by few groups in today's world.

GROUP LEADERS NEED YOUR SUPPORT

It's not an easy job to try to keep everyone in a group from going too fast. In any given session, there are usually one or two individuals who are feeling good and want to increase the pace. By restraining these exuberant individuals at the beginning, the leader will not only help those who aren't feeling good: all members of the group will benefit from the chemistry of keeping the whole group together. Even the frisky ones will benefit. Instead of slowing down later and suffering due to the fast early pace, they will feel strong to the end and will have the best chance of recovering quickly. Don't argue with your group leader when asked to slow down and stay together... even if it's a bad hair day or your blood sugar is low.

DESIGNATED SWEEPER

Even when the pacing is perfect, there are rare occasions when individuals cannot keep up with the group due to injury, sickness, etc. In each group, each week, a designated sweeper should drop back and stay with that person, providing support or transportation as needed. This assignment will rotate each week and is seldom needed with proper pacing for the group as a whole.

THE VICTORY CELEBRATION

One of the highlights of our Galloway group training is the celebration after the medals have been won. This gathering is filled with the exuberance of group victory, fun awards and war stories (some of them actually true). This one event brings together the positive emotions and collective respect into an experience that reinforces the great accomplishment.

Be prepared to share stories and to laugh. Your homework is to take notes on each group outing. Bring your disposable camera. There are always a few interesting things that happen, experiences shared and statements made. Just a few of those details, photos and quotes will spice up a great event.

173

PACE CHART

Mile Pace	2 mile	5 mile	10 mile	13 mile	Half marathon	15 mile	20 mile	Marathon
5:00	10:00	25:00	50:00:00	1:05:00	1:05:30	1:15:00	1:40:00	2:11:00
5:20	10:40	26:40	53:20:00	1:09:20	1:09:52	1:20:00	1:46:40	2:19:44
5:40	11:20	28:20	56:40:00	1:13:40	1:14:14	1:25:00	1:53:20	2:28:28
6:00	12:00	30:00	60:00:00	1:18:00	1:18:36	1:30:00	2:00:00	2:37:12
6:20	12:40	31:40	1:03:20	1:22:20	1:22:58	1:35:00	2:06:40	2:45:56
6:40	13:20	33:20	1:06:40	1:26:40	1:27:20	1:40:00	2:13:20	2:54:40
7:00	14:00	35:00	1:10:00	1:31:00	1:31:42	1:45:00	2:20:00	3:03:24
7:20	14:40	36:40	1:13:20	1:35:20	1:36:04	1:50:00	2:26:40	3:12:08
7:40	15:20	38:20	1:16:40	1:39:40	1:40:26	1:55:00	2:33:20	3:20:52
8:00	16:00	40:00	1:20:00	1:44:00	1:44:48	2:00:00	2:40:00	3:29:36
8:20	16:40	41:40	1:23:20	1:48:20	1:49:10	2:05:00	2:46:40	3:38:20
8:40	17:20	43:20	1:26:40	1:52:40	1:53:32	2:10:00	2:53:20	3:47:04
9:00	18:00	45:00	1:30:00	1:57:00	1:57:54	2:15:00	3:00:00	3:55:48
9:20	18:40	46:40	1:33:20	2:01:20	2:02:16	2:20:00	3:06:40	4:04:32
9:40	19:20	48:20	1:36:40	2:05:40	2:06:38	2:25:00	3:13:20	4:13:16
10:00	20:00	50:00	1:40:00	2:10:00	2:11:00	2:30:00	3:20:00	4:22:00
10:20	20:40	51:40	1:43:20	2:14:20	2:15:22	2:35:00	3:26:40	4:30:44
10:40	21:20	53:20	1:46:40	2:18:40	2:19:44	2:40:00	3:33:20	4:39:28
11:00	22:00	55:00	1:50:00	2:23:00	2:24:06	2:45:00	3:40:00	4:48:12
11:20	22:40	56:40	1:53:20	2:27:20	2:28:28	2:50:00	3:46:40	4:56:56
11:40	23:20	58:20	1:56:40	2:31:40	2:32:50	2:55:00	3:53:20	5:05:40
12:00	24:00	1:00:00	2:00:00	2:36:00	2:37:12	3:00:00	4:00:00	5:14:24
12:20	24:40	1:01:40	2:03:20	2:40:20	2:41:34	3:05:00	4:06:40	5:23:08
12:40	25:20	1:03:20	2:06:40	2:44:40	2:45:56	3:10:00	4:13:20	5:31:52
13:00	26:00	1:05:00	2:10:00	2:49:00	2:50:18	3:15:00	4:20:00	5:40:36
13:20	26:40	1:06:40	2:13:20	2:53:20	2:54:40	3:20:00	4:26:40	5:49:20
13:40	27:20	1:08:20	2:16:40	2:57:40	2:59:02	3:25:00	4:33:20	5:58:04
14:00	28:00	1:10:00	2:20:00	3:02:00	3:03:24	3:30:00	4:40:00	6:06:48
14:20	28:40	1:11:40	2:23:20	3:06:20	3:07:46	3:35:00	4:46:40	6:15:32
14:40	29:20	1:13:20	2:26:40	3:10:40	3:12:08	3:40:00	4:53:20	6:24:16
15:00	30:00	1:15:00	2:30:00	3:15:00	3:16:30	3:45:00	5:00:00	6:33:00
15:20	30:40	1:16:40	2:33:20	3:19:20	3:20:52	3:50:00	5:06:40	6:41:44
15:40	31:20	1:18:20	2:36:40	3:23:40	3:25:14	3:55:00	5:13:20	6:50:28
16:00	32:00	1:20:00	2:40:00	3:28:00	3:29:36	4:00:00	5:20:00	6:59:12
16:20	32:40	1:21:40	2:43:20	3:32:20	3:33:58	4:05:00	5:26:40	7:07:56
16:40	33:20	1:23:20	2:46:40	3:36:40	3:38:20	4:10:00	5:33:20	7:16:40
17:00	34:00	1:25:00	2:50:00	3:41:00	3:42:42	4:15:00	5:40:00	7:25:24
17:20	34:40	1:26:40	2:53:20	3:45:20	3:47:04	4:20:00	5:46:40	7:34:08
17:40	35:20	1:28:20	2:56:40	3:49:40	3:51:26	4:25:00	5:53:20	7:42:52
18:00	36:00	1:30:00	3:00:00	3:54:00	3:55:48	4:30:00	6:00:00	7:51:36

INSPIRATION
THE INCREDIBLE MOTIVATION
IN RUNNING FOR OTHERS

By Donna Hicken

*T*here are times like tonight (it's 4 am) when I finally give in to the fact that I am not going to sleep. Race routes, shoe contracts and runners of all shapes and sizes are pounding a path through my brain. Of all the unlikely turns my life could take, I would have put marathon founder right up there with rocket scientist. But then I would have said the same thing about living with breast cancer.

In 1999, I was diagnosed with the first of two bouts with the disease. At the time, I had just completed the Boston Marathon. Ironically, I ran for the Dana Farber team, raising money for breast cancer research. In so many ways, that diagnosis was the beginning of my life as I know it now.

As a news anchor for more than 20 years, I am used to living my life in public. All of my life. There are times when I frankly find that exhausting. But when I was diagnosed with breast cancer, it was a lifeline for me. So much support from so many people kept me going through the chemo and the baldness and the fatigue. I felt as if I was running the marathon of my life with a huge crowd on the street screaming "Go Donna! You can do it!!" I also found myself offering encouragement to other people who were running the same course with me, only without the same advantages.

I learned how many didn't have insurance. Many couldn't afford to pay for their medications and their mortgages at the same time. When they needed to focus on surviving, to take care of their children, they spent more time worrying about putting food on the table, today.

In my book *"The Good Fight,"* which chronicles my on-line breast cancer journal and the relationships that followed, I recounted the story of a woman named Robin. She's a breast cancer survivor who lost her Medicaid after her husband's truck broke down forcing him to buy a used one for his work in construction.

Robin is a pistol. She says it like it is. She and Glenn have five kids and they both work their tails off to support them. Like so many people, they let their insurance lapse during a particularly tough financial month and, of course, that's when she got the diagnosis. The treatment she received from both the medical community and the government was appalling.

"You'll be lucky if I treat you," one doctor told her, his picture of Jesus on the wall behind him. "I'm not going to make a dime."

This was while her Medicaid was still intact. After the truck incident, Robin couldn't complete her reconstructive surgery and couldn't get her follow-up medications.

"If I don't take that medicine, my cancer might come back and I could die," she explained to the woman at the Medicaid office.

"I guess you should have thought about that before you had five children," the clerk shot back.

The story made me livid then as it does now. Robin's story is one of thousands out there. Sometimes they should have been treated better by the people who are already in place to serve, but, many times, life circumstances simply left these women running their own lonely marathons.

That is why I started The Donna Hicken Foundation in June of 2003. I like to think of it as the crowd that carries these women along and makes them believe that they can finish the race. DHF funds the critical needs of underserved women with breast cancer. Whether it is paying for nausea medications or child care or utility bills, the goal is to help them focus on getting better, instead of on just getting by.

In the years since DHF was founded, we have served hundreds of women. When I have one of those days when I just want to draw the shades on my fishbowl, I pull out the letters I've received, like Johna's, who believe they are alive today in every sense of the word because of the service we provide.

"My name is Johna. I am a single parent of two, fighting the battle of breast cancer. The battle is not only health, it's financial, too. I am a survivor not only from my treatments, but without the help from The Donna Hicken Foundation, I would have lost my home. They helped me with my bills (light and phone bills and school clothes for my two children and other types of help with

odds and ends). I am so thankful for them. If they were not there, I would have lost my battle. We do need more foundations like The Donna Hicken Foundation for people who need help to stay on their feet.

Thank you again!" Johna

"I am a cancer patient with 3 young children. I needed chemotherapy and radiation to battle the recurrence. During treatment, my husband's employment was terminated. Without financial relief, my family would not make it. The Donna Hicken Foundation helped us by paying our mortgages, preschool, and medical bills for a month. What this gave us was time, the most precious gift of all. Our family is so grateful to this much needed charity." Christine, Todd, Owen, Reed and Cara

That last quote from Christine brings it all home for me. How precious is time? Runners are often obsessed with it. Battling a life-threatening disease certainly gave me a new perspective on making every second count. Asking people to run with me to help women with breast cancer seems like a perfect fit.

My "Run With Donna" team started small. We sold shirts as a fundraiser and asked people to wear them in the Gate River Run. It's Jacksonville's biggest race and the 15K national championship. Hundreds of people joined us!

That's how I met Jeff Galloway. As a long time marathoner I had, of course, admired Jeff, but I can't say I had actually bought in to his famous run/walk/run method. I was always one of those runners who wouldn't even consider walking during runs. That was sissy stuff. Plus, as a mostly solitary runner, the thought of training with a group sounded like work to me. But when Jeff approached me one day at the Gate River Run Expo and offered to train a team for my Foundation, I jumped at the opportunity.

Jeff told me if we were successful the first year, we could talk about rolling out the fundraiser on a more national scale. The definition of success, he told me: more than ten people who completed the fund-raising goal. Jeff came to Jacksonville for our kick-off. More than 70 people showed up that first night to hear him talk. I watched their eyes as they watched Jeff. People who had run dozens of marathons but had "retired" due to repeated injuries from over-training heard him describe how, with his method, they could run injury-free. People who had never run a step and never dreamed they could run a marathon heard how many of Jeff's followers had come right off the couch and completed the training and the race. People who were there because their mother or sister or they themselves had faced breast cancer heard him talk about the joy and sense of purpose that come with running for a cause.

One woman in particular drew my attention. She had a determined look on her face and just kept nodding. Her name was Andee. She had been a runner previously but had suffered a stroke. "My doctor told me I should just resign myself to a life without running," she said.

But Andee was having none of it. She had worked hard to overcome her limitations and was determined to get back on the road. Jeff's program sounded doable. Andee signed up that night. We would go on to add another eighty-five people.

There was Ike, a soft spoken, cherub-faced cop who started off with the idea of running the half marathon. His nine year old daughter set him straight. "If Ms. Donna Hicken can run that whole marathon, Daddy, then you should too," she ordered. I found out later that Ike was running, in part, to make a positive out of a huge negative in his life. He had just lost his son.

And there was Robert who was running for his mom, a recent breast cancer survivor. "I can't wait to go home and write my fund-raising letter," he told me the night of our first meeting. He was so proud of his mom and so emotional about her fight and doing something to help others.

Each runner committed to raising a thousand dollars for the cause. Each one had a unique reason for running.

From the first run with our Galloway trainers Chris and Amanda, I was hooked. It was the wildest thing. It was as if every person in the group had been hand-picked to be there. My husband's mantra is that we are all connected. Boy, did that ever become evident during those weeks and months of training. These people literally came from all walks of life, incredibly diverse in their interests, their incomes, their jobs and their zip codes. But every one had something to offer someone else. We all became therapists for one another. It was the running joke (pun intended) that what happens in the group stays in the group.

As our miles began to add up and we got closer to our goal, our teammate Miles Powell would write the miles completed on a big poster and we'd all get behind it for a picture at the end of the run. Twelve miles, 15, 18, 23! His wife Lisa, I call her the team mom, didn't run with us, but she always kept our keys and made sure everyone got in safely. She even cooked for us!

I will never forget the day we finished our 26-mile training run at the Baldwin Trail in west Jacksonville. Lisa cooked a complete Cajun feast that you could smell three miles from the finish line. It was incentive to finish quickly so the fast group wouldn't eat it all! Everyone finished the run feeling great and stood proudly behind Miles best sign yet: 26 miles! Andee crossed the finish line and received her medal for completing the Galloway program along with the rest

177

of us. She dropped to her knees and started crying. Then got up and pumped her fists in the air in triumph!

"A year ago I had a stroke, and today I just ran 26.2 miles, praise God," she beamed.

It was one of the most inspiring things I've seen. A month later she would repeat the feat at the Jacksonville Marathon. Jeff's run/walk/run method had allowed her to train for the race without overtaxing her body. In fact, every one of our teammates who stepped to the starting line that day successfully finished either the marathon or the half marathon. Every one.

The best part physically for me as an average runner was that I was able to get the miles in and I was literally never sore. We've all seen marathoners the day after a race. It becomes a titanic effort to simply step off a curb. Not with Jeff's program.

But before I give you the impression that Jeff's method only works for beginning or average runners, let me share with you that my husband qualified for Boston for the first time in a decade using the run/walk/run method, and, in fact, had negative splits through the second half of the marathon. His legs felt so fresh by mile 18, when most runners are hitting the wall, he just ran it in the rest of the way.

As I write this, we are in the middle of our second year with the group. We've doubled our number from last year. You should see us running down the road together. We need a traffic cop. Fortunately for us, we have a number of Jacksonville's finest on our team. A friend of mine recently joked that we've started our own cult. I don't know about cult, but I will confess to being happily addicted. I can now train for as many races as I could reasonably hope to run and avoid overuse injuries. Plus, I've made some really great friends.

I don't believe I am exaggerating at all when I say this program is transforming lives. Not just the lives of the hundreds of women we help through DHF, but the lives of the people running.

Taking it to the Next Level

I thought for certain Jeff would laugh at me the day I called him and said, "You know, there really isn't a marathon out there for breast cancer. What do you say we start our own?"

The thought had been in the back of my mind since Jeff's comments about taking our efforts to the next level. Then one morning, I was having coffee at Starbucks with my good friend Dr. Edith Perez. Edith is one of my favorite running partners, and she also happens to be the doctor who saved my life. Twice.

Edith is one of the top breast cancer researchers in the world. She is responsible for writing a clinical trial that produced what is arguably the greatest breakthrough against breast cancer in 30 years.

It combines a drug that targets a particularly vicious type of breast cancer with chemotherapy. The result was a 52 percent decrease in recurrence, even among patients with advanced stages of the disease. Edith travels the globe constantly sharing her knowledge. For this, I have abandoned her given name and simply refer to her these days as "rock star." On this morning, we were having a discussion about the fact that funding for clinical trials is getting tougher and tougher to come by. That's when the light bulb went on.

"Edith, you know I've wanted to grow my 26.2 With Donna team," I said. "What if DHF partnered with Mayo Clinic? I'd have my national connection and more funding for my Foundation, and you'd have the money you need to keep finding new ways to keep me alive?" This is my constant reminder to Edith that her number one priority is to keep me breathing.

If you could see the eyes on this woman, you'd know why I am sure she will find a cure for breast cancer. They light up like a child's on Christmas morning whenever she talks about new advances.

"Donna, this is FANTASTIC!" Edith's words flew out at me with such force that they almost knocked me off my chair. "Let's do it," she said. "We'll make this happen."

Her energy gave me the courage to approach Jeff later that morning. But to my surprise he didn't laugh. I'll never forget his initial response. "There is an untapped gold mine of support for this cause."

So that day, February 27th, 2006 we began mining for gold. Gold to help women in need survive their breast cancer. And gold to help Edith and other talented researchers eradicate the threat for future generations. Make no mistake, for all of our wonderful advances, thousands of women still die from breast cancer every year. Incredible women like my friend Susan Mehrlust. Susan passed away in December of 2006, ten years after the doctors told her she had six

months to live. She was a fighter and lived by the mantra that "each day is a gift". As a coach for many years, Susan always told her team to "play to the last point." No matter how far down you are, play hard until the very end.

That was the message and the way Susan lived her life. She didn't know how to have a bad day and spent every moment helping other women face the disease with courage. Susan was a constant reminder of what sheer will can do. We need women like Susan here among us. Beating the odds as she did, she still died way too young at 59. She is the perfect example of why we run and why this marathon came to be.

Our first race is set for February 17th, 2008 in Jacksonville Beach. Our course is a beautiful trek across the Intracoastal Waterway and along the roads that border the Atlantic Ocean. We even have a two-mile stretch on our hard-packed sands that couldn't be more perfect for running. 26.2 with Donna The National Marathon to Fight Breast Cancer is the only marathon in the country dedicated solely to wiping out breast cancer in our lifetime and to caring for those living with the disease right now.

So much to plan. Who has time for sleep?

179

RESOURCES

What To Look For In
A Training Program

As the half or full marathon has become a lifestyle change project, training groups are springing up all over North America. Because of the group support, training can become fun and your chance of completing these events is greatly increased. Because there is a wide range of groups, look for programs which offer the following:

- Training Groups, based upon fitness level

- A leader in each pace group who enforces a slow pace and the breaks

- A schedule which gradually increases the longest training session past "the wall"

- Long workouts every other weekend (every third weekend when long one reaches 18 to 20 miles)

- Lots of laughs on every group session

Go to www.jeffgalloway.com for

- Information on training groups in many North American cities call 1-800-200-2771
- Up-to-date training information and tips, training group gatherings and more.
- FREE Enewsletter sign-up.

e-coaching *from Jeff Galloway*

- · *To Stay Motivated*

- · *To Reach the Finish – Injury-Free*

- · *To Train for Your Time Goal*

182

Jeff Galloway's Beach Retreat Center Welcomes You!

Inspiration with information to accomplish your goal: INJURY FREE

On the panhandle of Florida, between Panama City and Ft. Walton Beach, is a unique area that is ideal for running most of the year: very white sand running beaches, 30+ miles of forest trails, a bike trail and several state parks adjacent to the beach.

Imagine finishing up an energy-filled run and then jumping in the pool! Jeff will instruct you in pool running, if you wish.

Jeff Galloway conducts week-end retreats there about once a month.

183

Jeff watches each person run and gives suggestions for better and faster running. He goes into the areas of building endurance, setting up a training program for various goals, nutrition, fat-burning, motivation, running faster, dealing with getting older and much more.

Jeff will help you set up a training program and will answer individual questions on site. Participants will have priority email access to Jeff after the retreat as they pursue their goals. Retreats are generally limited to 18 people. Some accommodations are available at or near the site.

For more info, go to JeffGalloway.com
contact Carol.Miller@jeffgalloway.com
or call 800/200-2771 x10.

www.JeffGalloway.com

Jeff Galloway's Fitness Vacations

TAHOE
July week and weekend

Join Jeff and his guests for a few days in beautiful Squaw Valley, on the north shore of Lake Tahoe.

- Our friendly presenters usually include

  Joe Henderson – running's most prolific writer who knows just about everything that's going on in our sport

  Bob Anderson – the expert who literally wrote the book on Stretching

  Sister Marion Irvine – the humorous and inspiring nun who qualified for the Olympic Trials at age 50

  Dr. Gary Moran – physiologist and expert in biomechanics, strength, etc.

  Dr. David Hannaford – sports podiatrist specializing in running injuries

- Everyone stays at the comfortable and beautiful Squaw Valley Lodge, with hot tubs, swimming, tennis, health club, etc.

- Retreat starts at 5:00 p.m. on Friday with an easy run to get acquainted.

- Each morning starts with a run or walk, whichever you choose (optional, of course), breakfast and then clinics by Jeff and his guests. Ask all the questions you wish.

- After lunch, you may shop, sight-see, sun by the pool or join the group for a scenic hike, T-shirt swap, etc.

- The group (@40) gathers again in the evenings for dinner onsite or at one of the nearby restaurants and after-dinner relaxing.

- All meals are included except for Saturday, Sunday & Wednesday dinners.

- Checkout is after breakfast on the last day.

Athens Marathon
October-November

Join us for the
Athens Marathon Tour

In 490 B.C., Phidippides ran from the battlefield of Marathon to Athens bringing news of victory. You can run the original route in his very footsteps.

Apostolos Greek Tours would like to be your host in Greece for the Marathon. Tour packages include:

- All Marathon entry paperwork and fees
- All ground transportation, all lodging and most meals in Greece
- Organized tours of ancient sites and museums including the Acropolis, Mycenae, Delphi and others
- Guest host and coach Jeff Galloway (proudly involved each year since 1995)
- Lots of activity and fun for non-runners too!
- Custom packages fit to your exact needs

For a free information packet, contact
Apostolos Greek Tours
2685 S. Dayton Way, #14
Denver, CO 80231
voice: 303/755-2888
fax: 303/755-4888
website: www.athensmarathon.com

INDEX

189

Jeff Galloway would like to join you on your next run

And the run after that, and the one after that.

Learn more about customized, daily Run-Walk-Run™ coaching with Jeff Galloway at
http://www.jeffgalloway.com/nextfit/

PRESS PLAY, GET FIT™

NOTES

NOTES

193

NOTES